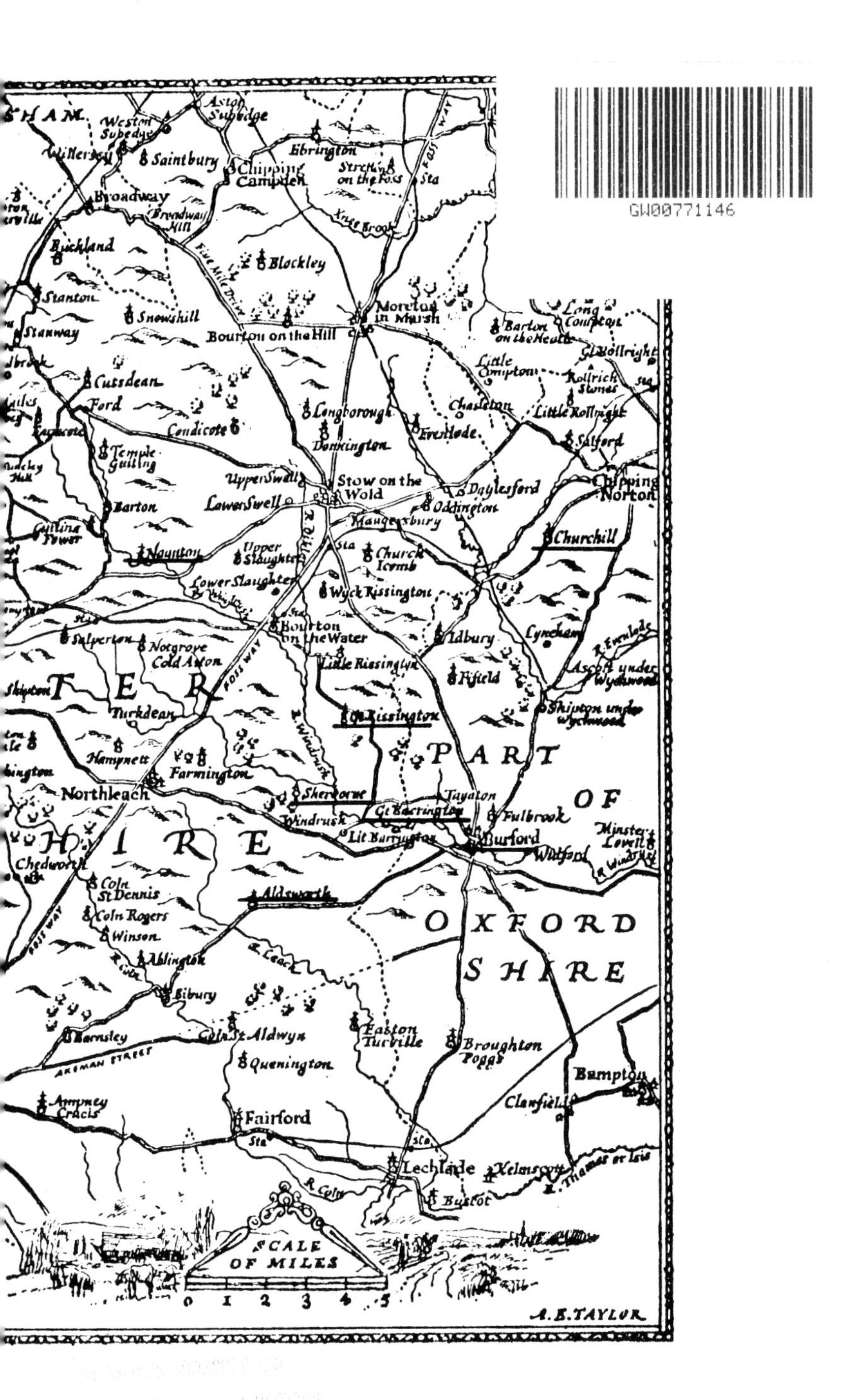
Aston Subedge
Weston Subedge
Willersey
Saintbury
Chipping Campden
Ebrington
Stretton on the Foss
Sta
Foss Way
Broadway
Broadway Hill
Knee Brook
Buckland
Blockley
Five Mile Drive
Stanton
Snowshill
Moreton in Marsh
Long Compton
Barton on the Heath
Stanway
Bourton on the Hill
Gt Rollright
Little Compton
Rollrich Stones
Cutsdean
Ford
Chasleton
Little Rollright
Longborough
Evenlode
Condicote
Temple Guiling
Donnington
Salford
Upper Swell
Stow on the Wold
Daylesford
Chipping Norton
Lower Swell
Oddington
Barton
Maugersbury
R. Dikle
Guiting Power
Nounton
Upper Slaughter
Church Icomb
Churchill
Lower Slaughter
Wyck Rissington
Bourton on the Water
Idbury
Lyneham
Salperton
Notgrove
Cold Aston
R. Evenlode
Little Rissington
Fifield
Ascott under Wychwood
T E R
Turkdean
R. Windrush
Gt Rissington
Shipton under Wychwood
Hampnett
Farmington
P A R T
Northleach
Sherborne
Taynton
O F
Windrush
Gt Barrington
Fulbrook
Lit Barrington
Burford
Minster Lovell
H I R E
Widford
R. Windrush
Chedworth
Coln St Dennis
Aldsworth
Coln Rogers
O X F O R D
Winson
R. Leach
Ablington
R. Coln
S H I R E
Bibury
Barnsley
Coln St Aldwyn
Easton Turville
Broughton Poggs
Akeman Street
Quenington
Bampton
Ampney Crucis
Clanfield
Fairford
Sta
Lechlade
Kelmscott
R. Thames or Isis
R. Coln
Buscot
SCALE OF MILES
0 1 2 3 4 5
A. E. TAYLOR
GW00771146

COTSWOLD YEOMEN AND SHEEP

The Garnes of Gloucestershire

Pen of Theaves. First prize at Chester, 21 July, 1858. Painter Richard Whitford.

COTSWOLD YEOMEN AND SHEEP

The Garnes of Gloucestershire

Richard O. Garne

Regency Press (London & New York) Ltd.
125 High Holborn, London WC1V 6QA

ISBN 0 7212 0710 3

Printed and bound in Great Britain by
Buckland Press Ltd., Dover, Kent.

Contents

List of Illustrations

Jacket Illustration
William Garne's champion Cotswold Ram RASE, 1851. Painted by W. H. Davis.

Genealogical Tables

Introduction

This is an attempt to trace the history of a small family of Yeomen of England from the middle ages to the present day on the Cotswold hills, at one time a remote and bleak area of England but now accessible and fashionable.

The object of this history is not to show from what illustrious stock the Garnes are descended, as is sometimes the motive for writing family histories, but rather to put on record as truthful an account as possible of the lives and relationships of this small family and the mark they made on the sheep and cattle of the world. It shows how for centuries the Garnes had flocks of Cotswold sheep, the wool of which was responsible for much of the prosperity of the nation in the middle ages and how but for the tenacity of Will Garne of Aldsworth in holding onto his flock for over thirty years when every other Cotswold flock in the country had ceased to exist there might now be no examples of this famous breed left.

Shorthorn cattle which were once seen on most of the farms of England and which are now very uncommon occupied the skill and ability of generation after generation of Garnes, so that after one hundred and sixty-seven years of continuous breeding the Garne pedigree was the oldest in England. Garne bulls had been exported to and stamped their type on herds in Australia, New Zealand, Argentine, Kenya, United States of America, South Africa, Russia and many other countries. In the Herd Book of 1892 there are no less than nine different Garnes on the Cotswolds with pedigree Shorthorn herds. The cattle were all related like their owners.

Although the family declined in numbers in the twentieth century with a gradual change into other occupations, in common with most farming families, the Yeoman vigour was still evident in the pioneering branch of the family which emigrated to Western Australia in the closing years of the nineteenth century, and who seventy years later were farming ten thousand acres and had a flock of five thousand sheep.

I do not suppose this history would ever have been written were it not for the extraordinary chain of coincidences which brought about the uniting of two of the main branches of the Garne family. This came about thus:—

My parents, my sister and I were living in East Kent with no knowledge of any other Garnes when my father died suddenly aged forty-one. My mother then set about earning her own living. She obtained a job as a school matron at Cirencester Grammar School, a place she had never previously heard of. While there she was taken ill and in the next bed of the hospital was a girl of thirteen called Barbara Garne, who had come in for only two days. Barbara's mother who called to see her daughter was surprised to find another Mrs. Garne so a friendship was struck up which continued by letter when my mother returned to East Kent. In consequence of this, many years later I was invited to spend a holiday with the Garnes on their farm at Aldsworth. Having very little money I cycled the two hundred miles from Dover to Aldsworth. While there I met Barbara Garne, her parents, brother and five sisters. When war broke out I joined the army and was posted to India and Burma. Some six years later while on demobilisation leave I called at Aldsworth to renew old friendships. It so happened that Barbara was staying with her parents for a few days holiday at the same time as my visit. Our friendship increased rapidly and we were married the following year.

I was naturally curious to know how or if we were related. So I was very relieved to find the relationship was as remote as our great great grandfathers having been brothers in 1790. Nevertheless once started on this research I found it so fascinating that I continued to collect facts for the next thirty-five years and this history is the result.

CHAPTER I

Early History

The Origin of the name

The first record that I can find of anyone with the name of Garne is that of Adam Garne or Adam de Garne, first Prior of St. Bartholomew's Abbey at Gloucester.

St. Bartholomew's Abbey was established about the year 1200 as a hospital for travellers and vagrants when the bridge was being built over the River Severn at Gloucester.

Adam Garne was chosen by the Bretheren and Sisters of the Abbey to be their head and he was confirmed as prior by Henry III in 1230 when the King was twenty-one. He gave St. Nicholas Church at the Westgate to the Brothers in 1228 and they rebuilt it. They wore a monastic habit and appear to have been well to do.

It is difficult to decide on the origin of the name Garne. The fact that these old records show it as de Garne implies that this Adam came from Garne, since there was a village of Garn near Westbury-on-Severn, only nine miles from Gloucester in the thirteenth and fourteenth centuries. A village which disappeared from records in about 1506, and is now only recalled in Garn's Hill, Westbury.

Then again there is the Garne river which ran near the Longhope hamlet of Abenhall, a branch of the Westbury Brook above Flaxley village running into the River Severn.

It was not until the latter part of the fourteenth century that surnames became fixed and passed from father to son. But as early as 1230 this Adam could have been known as Adam from Garn when in Gloucester and Adam Prior when in the village of Garn. Moreover other men from Garn would have been named de Garn and been no relation whatever.

In Wales a Garn is a hill or mountain so that today you find the Garn

Cafe or Garn Inn or Garn Farm in Wales. There is the Garn flock of Clun sheep owned by the Price family.

In Wales surnames did not come into general use till 1550 or even later, the prefix "ap" was used to denote the "son of" up till that time and as there are records of the name Garne in Gloucestershire in 1462 I rule out the likelihood of Welsh extraction.

In Herefordshire the word garn also means the garden. Large

Gloucester Cathedral from the old West Bridge and Gate.

numbers of English surnames derive from place names so the most likely origin of the name is Adam from Garne (village).

Of course it is quite impossible to say whether this Adam Garne was of Norman, Welsh or English extraction or a mixture of all three.

The spelling Garne or Garn is of no significance as spelling did not become standardised until the middle of the nineteenth century. It is such a relief for the geneologist to have to deal with a simple name like Garne which is also uncommon. Even the name Shakespeare was spelt five different ways.

The Middle Ages

In common with most other families it is extremely difficult if not impossible to trace the origins of a family before the fifteenth century. For a start there is the problem that surnames were only just coming in to general use at that time. Throughout the middle ages England was divided up into Manors which were small village communities and practically the only records to survive are the Manor Court Rolls—always written in Latin on rolls of parchment in a style of handwriting very difficult to decipher.

It is always worth taking note of family stories that have been passed down by word of mouth. One of these appeared in the obituary notice of Thomas Garne of Sherborne who died in 1873. It read "The Garne family, of French origin, after a residence in Ireland, settled in the fifteenth century with the Sherborne family in Gloucestershire". However it is difficult to find any documentary support for this theory. Often such stories are the result of conjecture. In Victorian times many people liked to believe their family came to England with the Normans. So that frequently there is no basis of fact whatever in these stories which are nevertheless passed down from generation to generation without anyone checking the facts.

There is no proof that anyone called Garne came from Ireland in the fifteenth century but the evidence so far (and the beauty of family history is that fresh facts are always turning up and altering previously held theories) is that Garnes were in Gloucestershire right through the middle ages.

From earliest times from long before the time of the Norman conquest practically the whole population lived on manors which were later given to Norman knights for military services; what became known as the feudal system, although there were large numbers of manors owned by monastries. All the manor lands were farmed in open fields with no fences by three classes of people:—

(a) The freemen who had small holdings of a few acres.

(b) The villeins who made up about half the population. They were required to work on the Lords land for so many days a year according to the size of their holding for which they paid no rent. This was usually a virgate or about thirty acres. This would be in strips scattered about the common fields of the village. There were three large fields, one wheat, one barley, oats or peas and one fallow. In addition a villein would have pasture rights on the village commons. Sometimes he employed others on his holding.

(c) The serfs who made up about a quarter of the population. These were the descendants of the enslaved inhabitants of Roman Britain who cultivated a few acres and hired themselves out for wages, making a very poor living.

The evidence for Garnes being in Gloucestershire in the middle ages rests on the existence of Adam Garne in 1230 as shown in Chapter I and the mention of the name in the Manor Court Rolls of 1462.

Life in the villages of England went on with only slow change until the Black Death of 1348, which had an enormous effect. It is possible that as much as half the population of the Cotswolds and in fact the whole nation died in the epidemic. This meant that those surviving were in tremendous demand to cultivate the land and look after the Lord's livestock. Slowly the villeins were able to buy their freedom from working on the Lord's land, to paying rent for their holdings and being paid wages for work done. In 1350 half the population of the country were not free but by 1600 there were no serfs or bondmen left.

The class of Yeoman had slowly come about, men who held their land either freehold or copyhold as tenants of a manor. Copyhold often meant a lease for three lives, so that land would be passed from father to son. This was often a virgate of thirty acres.

Copyhold tenants were customary tenants whose property automatically descended to the eldest son. Original copyhold tenants were villeins who were granted land in exchange for working on the manorial demesne. Labour services were commuted to a cash payment or quit rent.

The fact that Garnes were copyholders on the Winchcombe Monastic Estate before the Reformation adds weight to the theory that they were villeins in the middle ages who had slowly improved their position.

Another major effect of the Black Death on the Cotswolds was the shift from corn growing to sheep, thus promoting the wool trade, which provided much of the wealth of England during the middle ages. Mediaeval Cotswold wool was amongst the finest in Britain and in Europe; but it is a mystery what the type of sheep were, since there are no pictures or descriptions in existence. It is thought that they were a small short wooled breed which had been on the Cotswolds since Roman times. These were crossed with rams of the large Flemish breed by the Cistercian monks of Kingswood Abbey. These rams were part of the dowry of Edward III's bride, Princess Phillipa of Hainault. The result was the "Lionbreed" of the Cotswolds with the distinctive forelock so well known in later centuries. The only "pictures" of these sheep to have come down are in the form of stone carvings such as those on Bibury Church.

Sheep had been important on the Cotswolds since Saxon times. Cirencester wool market was even mentioned in the Doomsday book in 1086.

The fact that Cotswold wool played an enormous part in the prosperity of the nation has always been fully acknowledged and is emphasised to this day by the fact that the Lord Chancellor of England in The House of Lords sits on a large bale of Cotswold wool covered in red cloth.

In 1306 St. Peter's Abbey at Gloucester had ten thousand sheep and the Abbot of Winchcombe had at least eight thousand sheep, one of the largest flocks in England. In the century up to 1360 Britain was exporting five thousand two hundred tons of wool annually. Most serfs kept a few sheep on the commons, the wool from which provided money with which to buy their freedom. In 1485 the Abbot of Winchcombe bought all his tenants' wool to sell with his own. The villein, whose forebears by slow accumulation and interchange had amassed a comfortable holding, now began to appear in his true light as a tenant farmer, an employer of labour. By the Dissolution of the monastries in 1539 nearly every yeoman had his little sheep flock.

The term Yeoman came into use at this time and remained up to the nineteenth century as the typical example of the independent country Englishman, the back-bone of the English nation. In subsequent centuries so many Garnes were described in records as "Yeoman" that it seemed necessary to elaborate on this way of life. Similarly Cotswold sheep were responsible for the livelihood and gradual improvement in

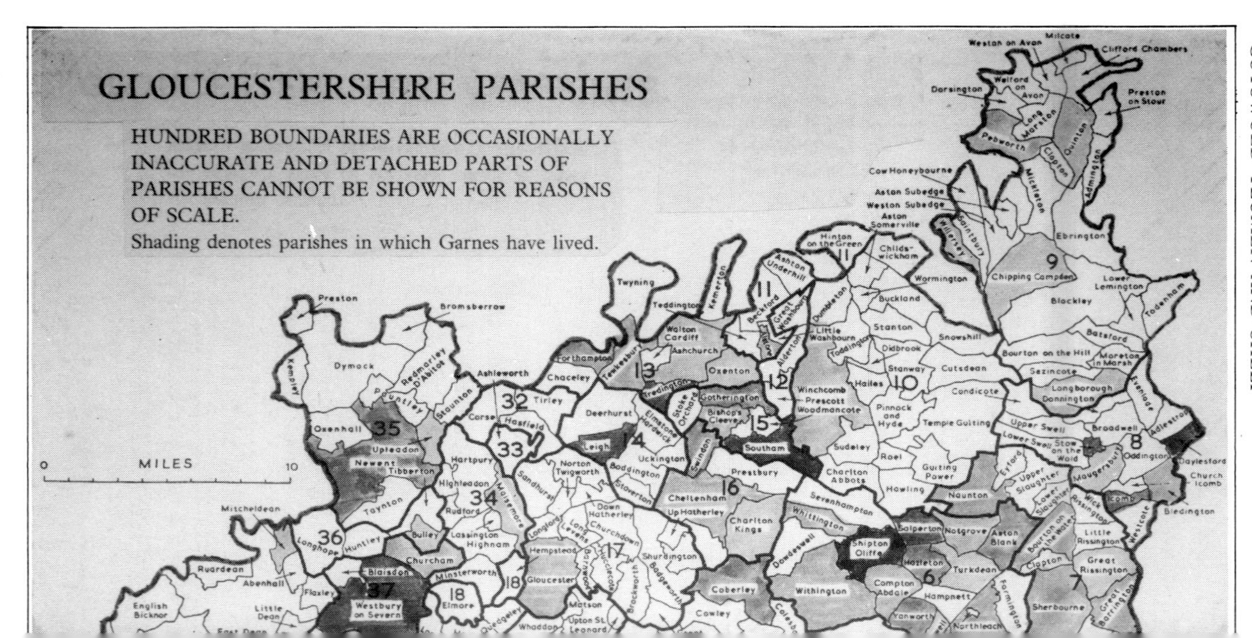
GLOUCESTERSHIRE PARISHES
HUNDRED BOUNDARIES ARE OCCASIONALLY INACCURATE AND DETACHED PARTS OF PARISHES CANNOT BE SHOWN FOR REASONS OF SCALE.
Shading denotes parishes in which Garnes have lived.
0
MILES
10
Weston on Avon
Milcote
Clifford Chambers
Dorsington
Welford on Avon
Preston on Stour
Long Marston
Pebworth
Quinton
Clapton
Admington
Cow Honeybourne
Aston Subedge
Weston Subedge
Aston Somerville
Mickleton
Saintbury
Willersey
Ebrington
Chipping Campden
Lower Lemington
Todenham
Blockley
Batsford
Hinton on the Green
Childswickham
Wormington
Ashton Underhill
Beckford
Great Washbourn
Dumbleton
Buckland
Twyning
Teddington
Kemerton
Little Washbourn
Toddington
Stanton
Snowshill
Bourton on the Hill
Moreton in Marsh
Walton Cardiff
Ashchurch
Alderton
Didbrook
Stanway
Cutsdean
Sezincote
Evenlode
Forthampton
Tewkesbury
Oxenton
Winchcomb
Hailes
Longborough
Donnington
Adlestrop
Preston
Bromsberrow
Kempley
Dymock
Redmarley D'Abitot
Ashleworth
Chaceley
Tredington
Stoke Orchard
Gotherington
Prescott
Woodmancote
Candicote
Pinnock and Hyde
Temple Guiting
Upper Swell
Broadwell
Daylesford
Staunton
Tirley
Deerhurst
Elmstone Hardwick
Bishop's Cleeve
Southam
Lower Swell
Stow on the Wold
Oddington
Church Icomb
Oxenhall
Upleadon
Corse
Hasfield
Leigh
Uckington
Swindon
Sudeley
Roel
Guiting Power
Eyford
Upper Slaughter
Maugersbury
Newent
Tibberton
Hartpury
Highleadon
Norton
Twigworth
Boddington
Staverton
Prestbury
Charlton Abbots
Hawling
Naunton
Lower Slaughter
Wick Rissington
Icomb
Westcote
Bledington
Taynton
Rudford
Maisemore
Sandhurst
Cheltenham
Up Hatherley
Sevenhampton
Little Rissington
Mitcheldean
Longhope
Huntley
Bulley
Lassington
Highnam
Longford
Down Hatherley
Churchdown
Long Levens
Charlton Kings
Whittington
Salperton
Notgrove
Aston Blank
Bourton on the Water
Ruardean
Abenhall
Churcham
Hempstead
Barnwood
Hucclecote
Shurdington
Dowdeswell
Shipton Oliffe
Hazleton
Turkdean
Clapton
Great Rissington
Blaisdon
Minsterworth
Gloucester
Brockworth
Badgeworth
English Bicknor
Little Dean
Flaxley
Westbury on Severn
Elmore
Matson
Upton St. Leonard
Coberley
Withington
Compton Abdale
Hampnett
Farmington
Sherbourne
Great Barrington
Cowley
Yanworth
Northleach
Whaddon

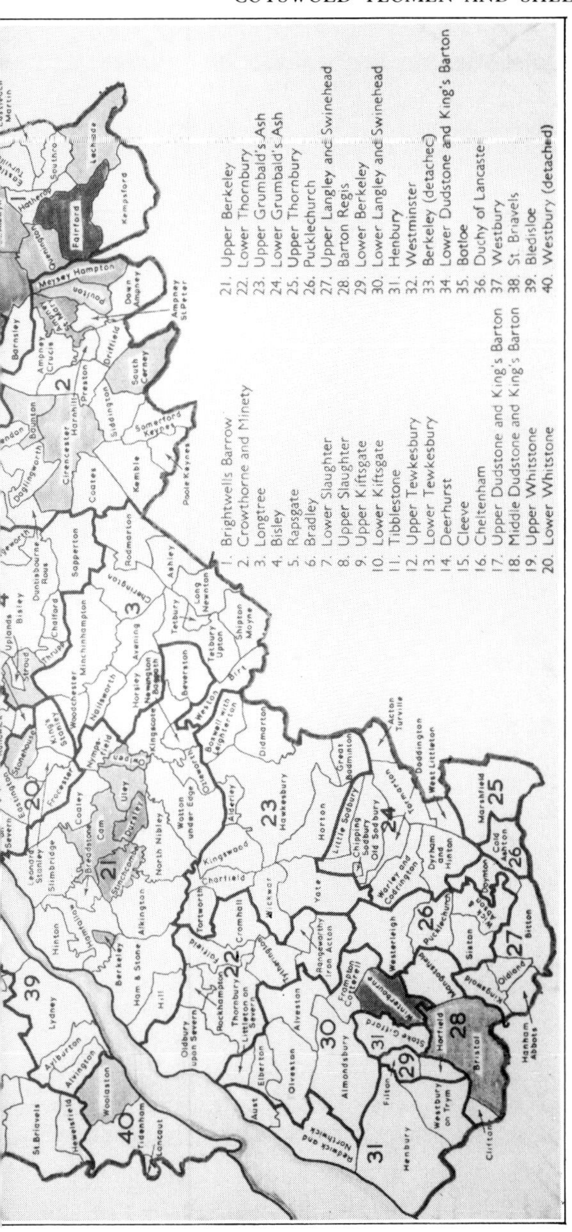
1. Brightwells Barrow
2. Crowthorne and Minety
3. Longtree
4. Bisley
5. Rapsgate
6. Bradley
7. Lower Slaughter
8. Upper Slaughter
9. Upper Kiftsgate
10. Lower Kiftsgate
11. Tibblestone
12. Upper Tewkesbury
13. Lower Tewkesbury
14. Deerhurst
15. Cleeve
16. Cheltenham
17. Upper Dudstone and King's Barton
18. Middle Dudstone and King's Barton
19. Upper Whitstone
20. Lower Whitstone
21. Upper Berkeley
22. Lower Thornbury
23. Upper Grumbald's Ash
24. Lower Grumbald's Ash
25. Upper Thornbury
26. Pucklechurch
27. Upper Langley and Swinehead
28. Barton Regis
29. Lower Berkeley
30. Lower Langley and Swinehead
31. Henbury
32. Westminster
33. Berkeley (detached)
34. Lower Dudstone and King's Barton
35. Botloe
36. Duchy of Lancaster
37. Westbury
38. St. Briavels
39. Bledisloe
40. Westbury (detached)

the lives of so many Garnes, in fact right up to the dispersal of the last remaining Cotswold flock in England in 1967, which belonged to Will Garne of Aldsworth.

It was common practice to write "Yeoman" after a man's name as it described status, that below gentleman and above tradesman. Yeomen seldom had much spare money, it was all tied up in land and livestock. They liked to be known as plain honest men with no ostentation, thrifty and frugal but never niggardly. They could rarely read or write and so few documents or records by yeomen have come down. They were usually known for good neighbourlyness, partly because in small communities it was essential for people to help each other. The work of organising the village was always voluntary and usually carried out by yeomen: Such tasks as that of constable responsible for maintaining law and order; overseer for administering the poor law and churchwarden with a wide range of duties.

Early Records

Up till now no earlier record of the name Garne has been found in Gloucestershire or anywhere else before 1462, which is not surprising since records of this period are very rare. They were always written on parchment which is sheep skin, often with a rough surface, inclined to be smelly and attacked by insects and mites. They were a dirty brown colour. Naturally they were not stored in ideal conditions but usually in damp cupboards or attics where moulds made them illegible. The earliest, following the Norman Conquest being written in Norman French, but after the time of Edward III in Latin. It was not till Georgian times that English was used in legal documents, although wills were written in English in Tudor times.

In the Manor Court Rolls of Pegglesworth, near Andoversford for 1462 William Garne and his wife, Elizabeth levied a fine of lands. In the next year at Greet or Gretton, near Winchcombe John Garne and Elizabeth his wife levied a fine of lands to Thomas Birge and others.

This expression "levied a fine of lands" always comes in documents known as "Feet of Fines". What started as a means of settling disputes came to be used for the transfer of land and the title of manors, lands and tenements in fee simple. These "Feet of Fines" are records of fictitious law suits entered into in order to avoid regulations restricting the conveyance of land and to provide written evidence. The intending purchaser was plaintiff who claimed the property from the vendor. In this way written title deeds of the transaction were preserved in the Manor Court Rolls.

So here we have evidence of two separate Garnes, William and John, buying land on the Cotswolds in the fifteenth century.

For the translation and recording of these Court Rolls I am indebted to the Bristol and Gloucester Archaeological Society who for many years have published the results of their research.

We have to go on ninety-two years for the next record to 3rd May, 1555, in the parish of Southam, near Tewkesbury when John Garne, a yeoman brought a lawsuit for false statements against Thomas Evans of Strensham in Worcestershire. (Vol. I page 296 Bristol and Gloucester Archaeological Society.)

Then in 1597 in the thirty-nineth year of Queen Elizabeth's reign there is a deed concerning John Garne of Naunton upon Cottiswolde in which Edward Aylworth, John Collett and John Talbot and Eleanor his wife have given to John Garne, James Robert, John Sheathe, Anthony and Thomas of Naunton the sum of £400. Plainly this sum was for the purchase of land in Naunton. (Vol. XVII page 165 Bristol and Gloucester Archaeological Society.)

In the parish of Mitcheldean in the Forest of Dean on the western county boundary there was a survey of the Manor in 1639, the Manor having been sold to Nicholas Roberts in 1619 for £2,000. One of the free tenants was William Garne, paying 5/- an acre for two acres.

This is the extent of early records which have come to light apart from a list of names made in 1608 of those men liable for service with the militia. This has been published under the title "Men and Armour for Gloucestershire 1608" by Smythe. In this list the name Garne appears three times (1) William Garne of Mitcheldean, probably the same man who was tenant of the two acres (2) Walter Garne of Oxenton, labourer, one Caliver (a weapon usually used by a short man) (3) Edward Garne of Salle Tythinge, Putley a farm servant to John Wooles, husbandman.

This list is valuable especially as Gloucestershire was the only county to publish such a list. But unfortunately yeomen and gentlemen usually managed to escape being called for the militia either by paying a fine or finding a substitute. Hence although for Sherborne parish there are 84 names, the name Garne is not mentioned. The estate owner William Dutton is described as gentleman and yeoman.

In 1600 the innkeeper at Compton Abdale is recorded as J. Garne.

The will of Richard Garne of Oxenton, died 1629

Richard Garne of Oxenton—1629

In the name of God Amen the three and twentieth day of January in the year of our Lord God 1629 for as much as all men are mortal and nothing man from death I Richard Garne of Oxenton in the county of Gloucester being sick in body yet thanks be given to God of good and powerful memory do make this my last will and testament in manner and form following: First I do bequeath my soul unto Almighty God my Creator: and to Jesus Christ his Son my Redeemer by whose death and passion I repose my whole trust of Salvation. And my—body I bequeath to be buried in the earth when it shall please God to call me to his mercy. Item I give and bequeath towards the repairing of the parish church of Oxenton five shillings: And to the poor people of the same parish five shillings. Item I do give and bequeath to my son Richard Garne six pounds to be paid within one year after the date hereof. Item I do give and bequeath unto Anne Garne my daughter six pounds to be paid within one year after the date hereof. Item I do give and bequeath unto Margery Whittle five shillings to be paid within one year next after the date hereof. Item All the rest of my—moveable and—my debts being paid and funeral expence discharged (excepting all the sheep that are marked with the mark of the said John Garne, Richard Garne and Anne Garne my daughter with and to them only use and uses) I wholly give and bequeath unto the said John, Richard and Anne my daughter and Anne my wife equally to be divided between them. And I do request my loving friends William Freeman and Nicholas Bent of Oxenton my overseers of this my last will and testament and for their pains to be taken hence I do give unto them sixty pence a year.
In witness whereof I have hereunto set my hand and seal the day and year aforesaid

Early Wills

There are wills in the Gloucester Record Office of four notable Garnes, i.e. those who were well enough off to make a will in the 17th century. These are (1) John Garne of Gotherington died in 1580 (2) John Garne of Naunton died 1611 (3) Joane Garne of Leigh died 1612 and (4) Richard Garne of Oxenton died 1629.

These wills are all written in English, apart from pieces in Latin by the Bishop's Court and all in Secretary hand which was in use from 1550 till 1700 before italic handwriting came in.

Some deductions can be made from reading these four wills, viz. The three men were yeomen. John Garne of Gotherington mentions four sons and three daughters, i.e. Richard William, Henry, Jhon, Katherine and Julien. After a list of bequests he leaves the residue to his loving and natural son, Jhon.

John Garne of Naunton who died in 1611 makes bequests to his brothers, Richard, William and Laurence and their children. He leaves his free land "which he purchased from Mr. John Talbot late Lord of the Manor of Naunton, to his nephew, Henry, son of his elder brother, Richard, and to his heirs males for ever and for want of such issue to the heirs male of the next Richard never to be alienated from the name of the Garnes".

It seems probable that John of Gotherington was the father of John of Naunton who in 1580 married Agnes Unton (an unusual name). She could have been connected with Sir Edward Unton who held Chedworth Manor in 1547. Then in 1595 John Garne of Naunton married Margaret Poule his second wife. His sole executrix was his wife, Margaret, who was to receive the rent of his free land.

Since Joane Garne of Leigh mentions her brothers, Laurence and William and nephews and nieces with the same names as those in John of Naunton's will the probablity is that she and John were brother and sister.

No conclusion can be reached about Richard Garne of Oxenton who died in 1629, except that he had a flock of sheep marked with the marks of his children, John, Richard and Anne. Since Oxenton is the next parish to Gotherington this Richard could be the grandson of John Garne of Gotherington and nephew of John of Naunton.

Unfortunately it is seldom possible to read the inscriptions on tombstones over three hundred years old. Neither is it possible to tie up any of the names in these four wills with entries in parish registers.

Parish Records

In 1538 Thomas Cromwell made it legal for parish priests to keep a record of baptisms, marriages and burials in their parishes.

At first this was rather casually carried out, if at all, in small books of vellum, which was a high quality parchment made of the skins of very young animals. Gradually paper was becoming obtainable made into books. Although there was a fine for failure to keep these records, they were often neglected. They were in the complete control of the parson and the parish clerk, who were often the only people in the parish who could write. Following the dissolution of the monastries and the teaching by the monks having been removed, the number of literate people fell. People only knew their own names orally and were dependant on the clerk or the parson to write as he thought. It is not surprising that most surnames were spelled differently every time they were entered. Luckily the name Garne does not allow for very much variation of spelling, so it always appears Garne or Garn. Just occasionally there is an 'S'.

I have only found three parishes in Gloucestershire with Garne entries in the parish records before 1600; Naunton, Bishops Cleeve and Upleadon right on the north-west of the county. There is also a baptism at Fritwell over the border in Oxfordshire in 1576.

During the seventeenth century the name appears in many more parishes, mostly on the Cotswolds as the family expanded, but a few at Stonehouse in the Stroud Valley. Parishes involved are:— Sherborne, Naunton, Turkdean, Compton Abdale, Salperton, Hazelton, Bishops Cleeve, Withington, Oxenton, Ashchurch and Stonehouse.

I have not been able to connect any of the names appearing in any of these parishes except for that of Sherborne.

It is quite possible that there were and still are families of Garn(e) entirely unrelated to the main line I have followed from Sherborne.

During the great national population increase of the nineteenth century the name Garn(e) appeared in numbers in Cheltenham, Bristol, London, Lancashire, Cheshire and the West Midlands. A few of these people no doubt came from the main Cotswold family although it is very difficult to prove. By 1980 however the name was once more very uncommon. There are very few copies of the Telephone Directories of England where the name appears. In Gloucestershire where once the family was most numerous, by 1983 the number of adults is down to thirteen, only two of whom are under sixty years old.

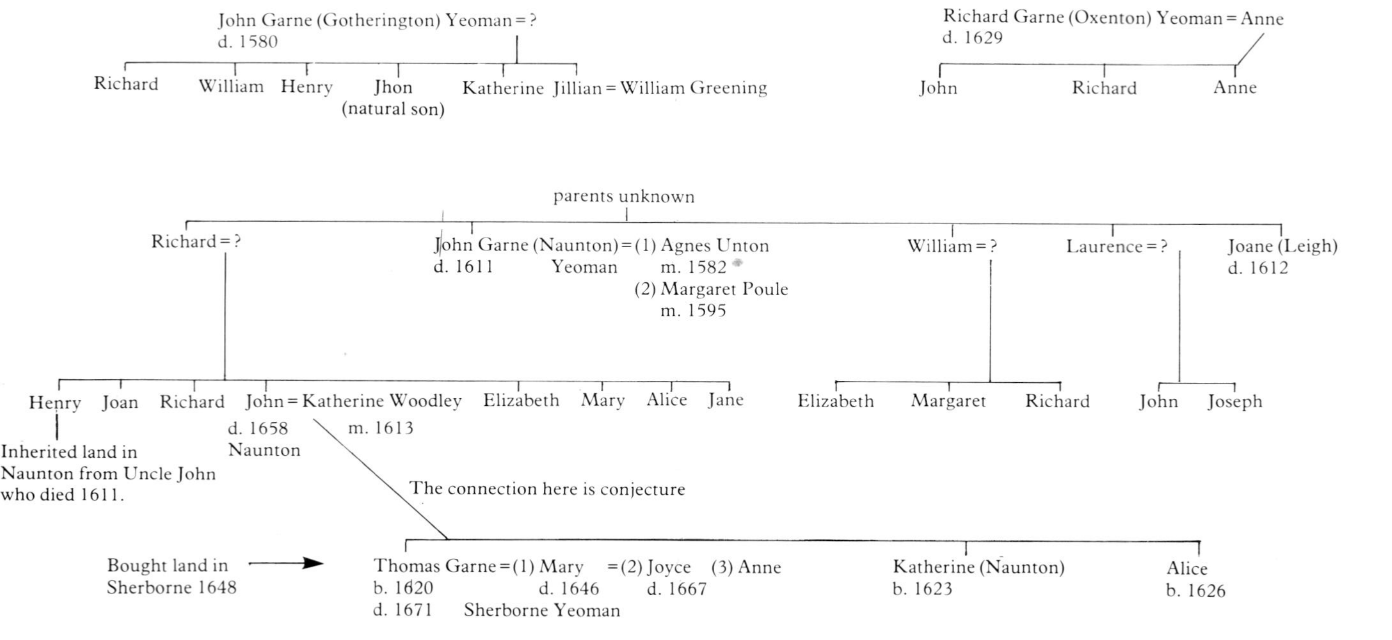
INFORMATION DERIVED FROM WILLS
Information from Court Rolls
William Garne = Elizabeth. Lived at Pegglesworth 1462.
John Garne = Elizabeth. Lived at Greet, Nr. Winchcombe 1463.
John Garne (Yeoman). Lived at Southam 1555.
John Garne (Gotherington) Yeoman = ?
d. 1580
Richard
William
Henry
Jhon
(natural son)
Katherine
Jillian = William Greening
Richard Garne (Oxenton) Yeoman = Anne
d. 1629
John
Richard
Anne
parents unknown
Richard = ?
John Garne (Naunton) = (1) Agnes Unton
d. 1611
Yeoman
m. 1582
(2) Margaret Poule
m. 1595
William = ?
Laurence = ?
Joane (Leigh)
d. 1612
Henry
Joan
Richard
John = Katherine Woodley
d. 1658
Naunton
m. 1613
Elizabeth
Mary
Alice
Jane
Elizabeth
Margaret
Richard
John
Joseph
Inherited land in
Naunton from Uncle John
who died 1611.
The connection here is conjecture
Bought land in
Sherborne 1648
Thomas Garne = (1) Mary
b. 1620
d. 1671
d. 1646
Sherborne Yeoman
= (2) Joyce
d. 1667
(3) Anne
Katherine (Naunton)
b. 1623
Alice
b. 1626

CHAPTER II

Sherborne

Sherborne is important in the history of the Garne family because it is from here that all branches of the Garne family stem. The descent can be traced with certainty from here for the last three hundred and thirty-five years for many members of the family living today.

This Sherborne, Gloucestershire, is only a small village on the north side of the Turnpike Road (now the A40) about midway between Cheltenham and Oxford. It is not to be confused with the well known town of the same name in Dorset.

Sherborne nestles in this Cotswold valley alongside the Sherborne Brook, a tributary of the River Windrush. It was for hundreds of years owned by Winchcombe Abbey, the largest of the thirteen parishes they owned. Their total estate was twenty-five thousand three hundred acres of which Sherborne is recorded as having thirty Hides or about three thousand six hundred acres. (A Hide was about one hundred and twenty acres.)

Sherborne was the headquarters of the Abbey flock of sheep where the annual sheep washing and shearing took place. This was a matter of considerable organisation and importance since the wool produced the bulk of the Abbey's income. The Abbot took charge and stayed in Sherborne Grange. It is on record that in 1485 two thousand nine hundred sheep were sheared. It is an interesting speculation that some of them could have been Garne sheep since the Abbey bought their tenants wool and exported it with their own.

Then came the Dissolution of the Monastries by Henry VIII and Winchcombe Abbey reverted to the ownership of the crown.

THE DESCENT OF THOMAS GARNE, SHERBORNE YEOMAN 1620-71

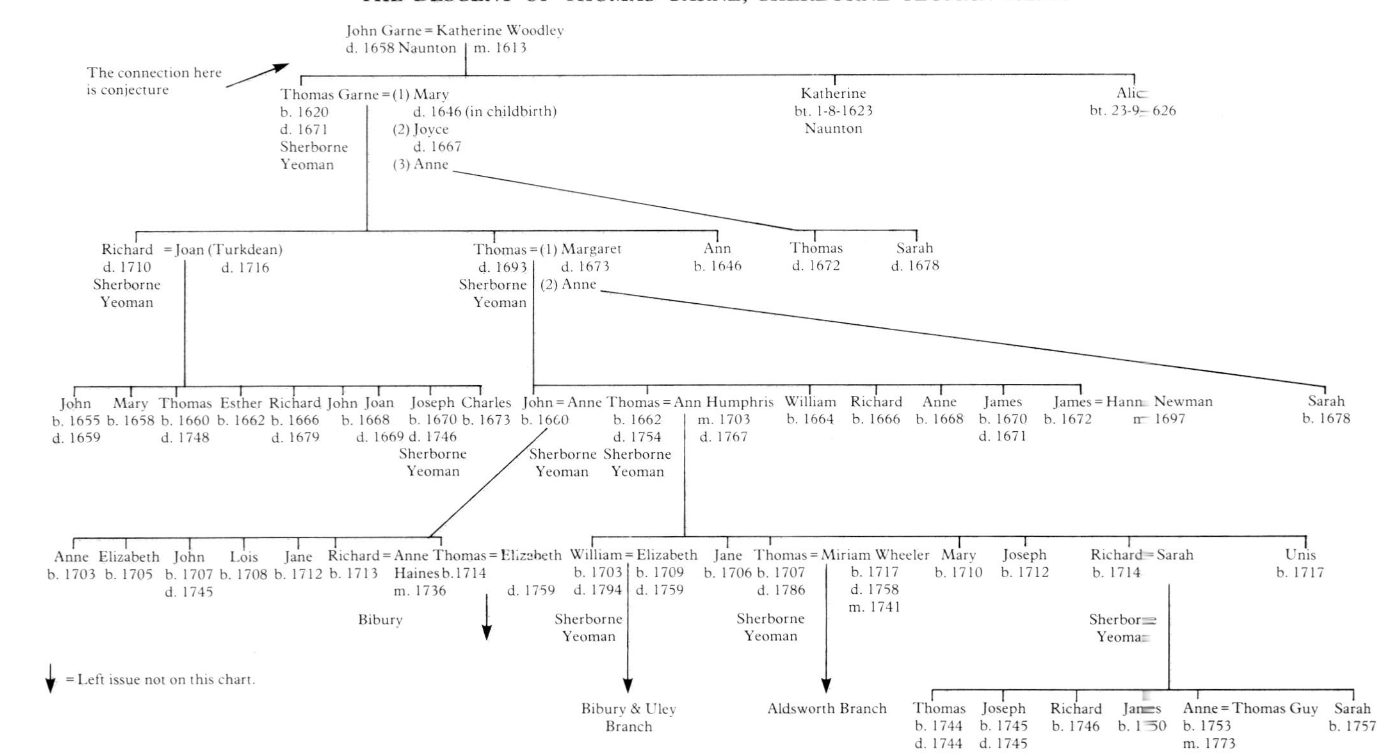

The Duttons

At about this time a Thomas Dutton of Cheshire, in return for his services to the King in relieving the garrison at Rothlain Castle in North Wales which was being attacked by the Welsh, became surveyor of crown lands in Gloucestershire, a very influential position.

We find that in 1551 this Thomas Dutton acquired the Manor of Sherborne. Twenty-six years later he obtained a lease of the Manor of Aldsworth, the adjoining parish which had belonged to Gloucester Abbey before the Dissolution. The freehold of Aldsworth was bought by Thomas Dutton's son, William in 1611.

The Dutton family, later Barons of Sherborne, continued to own the greater part of Sherborne and Aldsworth until the death of Charles Dutton, Lord Sherborne in 1983, a period of four hundred and thirty-two years for Sherborne and three hundred and seventy-two years for Aldsworth.

However there is no evidence that any Garne appeared on the estate till one hundred years after the Duttons arrived. Had they done so surely the name would have appeared in the parish registers?

Thomas Garne of Sherborne

The most valuable information of the Garnes of this period comes from the will of Thomas Garne of Sherborne made in 1693 in which he states that his father, Thomas Garne, had bought in 1648 two messuages (presumably houses with outbuildings and paddocks) and four yardlands from John Dutton (known as Crump Dutton, from his humpback). A yardland was thirty acres so this would have been one hundred and twenty acres, probably scattered round the parish in the open fields. This land was copyhold for three lives, that of the buyer, Thomas Garne, and his sons, Richard and Thomas. It is possible "Crump" Dutton needed the money having financially supported the Royalist cause in the civil war.

It is not possible to say whether this Thomas Garne moved to Sherborne because he had bought the land or whether he was living at Sherborne at the time and perhaps inherited the money. As parish records were only just starting at the time it is not possible to say where Thomas Garne came from. He may have been a son of John Garne of Naunton whose uncle owned land in that parish. Certainly his two sons, Richard and Thomas, remained on the land he had bought for the rest of their lives and the parish records show there were seventeen baptisms

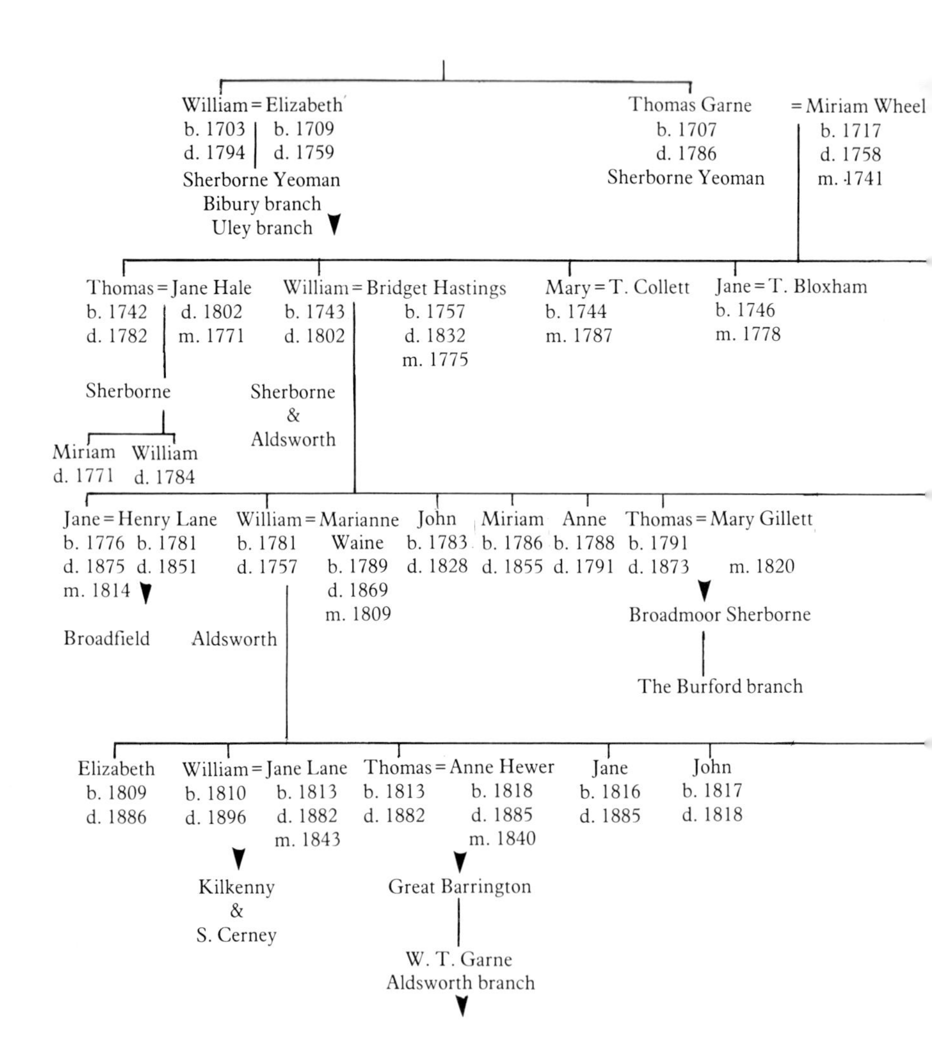
William = Elizabeth
b. 1703 b. 1709
d. 1794 d. 1759
Sherborne Yeoman
Bibury branch
Uley branch
Thomas Garne
b. 1707
d. 1786
Sherborne Yeoman
= Miriam Wheel
b. 1717
d. 1758
m. 1741
Thomas = Jane Hale
b. 1742 d. 1802
d. 1782 m. 1771
Sherborne
Miriam
d. 1771
William
d. 1784
William = Bridget Hastings
b. 1743 b. 1757
d. 1802 d. 1832
m. 1775
Sherborne
&
Aldsworth
Mary = T. Collett
b. 1744
m. 1787
Jane = T. Bloxham
b. 1746
m. 1778
Jane = Henry Lane
b. 1776 b. 1781
d. 1875 d. 1851
m. 1814
Broadfield
William = Marianne Waine
b. 1781 b. 1789
d. 1757 d. 1869
m. 1809
Aldsworth
John
b. 1783
d. 1828
Miriam
b. 1786
d. 1855
Anne
b. 1788
d. 1791
Thomas = Mary Gillett
b. 1791
d. 1873 m. 1820
Broadmoor Sherborne
The Burford branch
Elizabeth
b. 1809
d. 1886
William = Jane Lane
b. 1810 b. 1813
d. 1896 d. 1882
m. 1843
Kilkenny
&
S. Cerney
Thomas = Anne Hewer
b. 1813 b. 1818
d. 1882 d. 1885
m. 1840
Great Barrington
W. T. Garne
Aldsworth branch
Jane
b. 1816
d. 1885
John
b. 1817
d. 1818

THE ALDSWORTH BRANCH 1800-1900

The descent of William Garne of Wall Farm
All spelled Garne

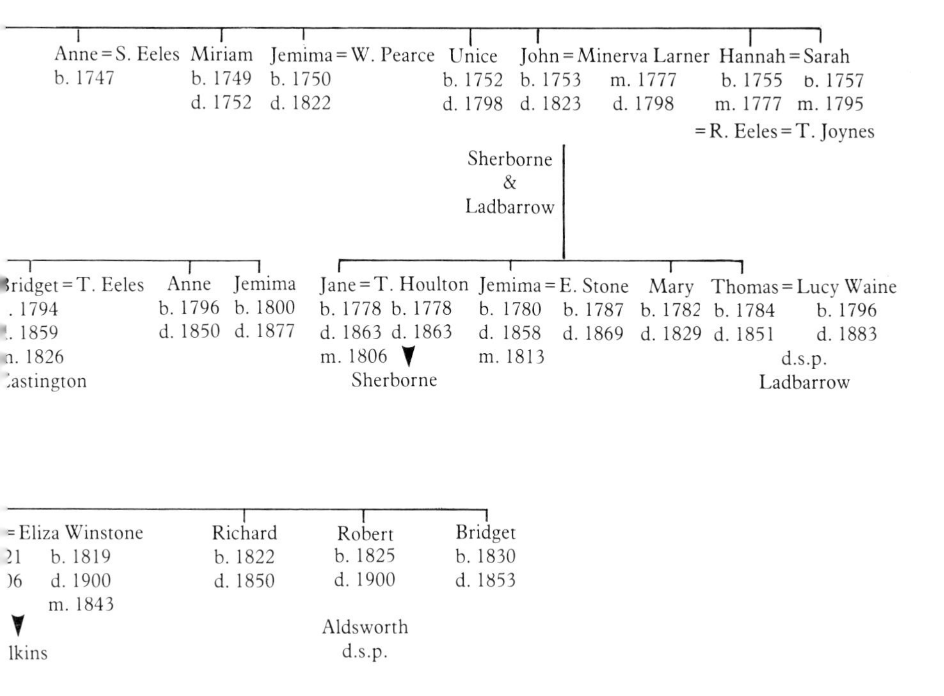

▼ = Left descendants not on this chart.
d.s.p. = Died without issue.

from 1655 to 1678 from the two families. These were the first of a long list of baptisms, marriages and deaths recorded in Sherborne registers for the next two hundred years until 1897.

Unfortunately no tenancy records of the Sherborne estate for this period survive, so it is not possible to say which families lived on which farms in the early years.

Early in the nineteenth century Lord Sherborne entrusted the keeping of the estate records to the parson while the mansion was being rebuilt. Unfortunately the parson did not appreciate the value of the old documents and frequently sold the leather covers and vellum sheets to the cobbler for repairing shoes. Years later many Sherborne papers were discovered in the vicarage attic and burnt by the housekeeper when spring cleaning.

By 1700 there were at least four families of Garnes living in Sherborne, all yeomen. From the seventeenth century onwards there were more large farms than small on the Cotswolds, so it seems probable these Garnes were all farming large acreages and employing others as well as their own families, living in substantial houses in the village, with single labourers living in the farmhouses with them.

Yeomen always kept stock since they had rights of common on the open commons. There were few fences or walls and children spent much of their time looking after the grazing cattle and sheep. Not many cattle could be kept owing to the problem of providing enough winter fodder from the hay made on the riverside meadows.

The farming cultivations were all done by oxen which were economical to feed and lived many years before being fattened for beef. A draught horse was rare.

Very few people at this time could read or write and certainly the Garne men who made wills signed their names with a cross. It was unusual for anyone to own enough to make a will, which is now the most valuable source of information.

The middle of the eighteenth century saw a boom in farming and plainly some of the Garne families of Sherborne were doing very well. Also there were many who left the district and are no doubt the ancesters of many of the Garnes scattered round the world today, but who have not traced their descent back to Sherborne.

Thomas Garne (1662-1754) married Ann Humphris of Cirencester in 1703 and lived to be ninety-two. In his will of 1754 he mentions all his children except his second son, Thomas, possibly because this

Thomas was already very well established. He it was who is the ancestor of the Aldsworth branch of the family. The eldest brother, William, was the ancestor of the Dursley branch.

The greatest change that had taken place for centuries came about in 1777 with the private act of parliament allowing Sir James Dutton to enclose the parish of Sherborne.

CHAPTER III

Aldsworth

Aldsworth is the next parish to Sherborne on the south side although the villages are about three miles apart. It is an upland parish, five to six hundred feet above sea level and rather bleak. Up until 1793 it had been cultivated on the open field system but there had been good unenclosed sheep pastures here since Saxon times, although little meadow land.

Enclosure

With the tremendous upsurge in interest in all matters to do with farming in the eighteenth century, particularly from the landowning classes and aristocracy, large numbers of private bills were laid before parliament to enclose the villages of England. Sherborne was enclosed in 1777 and Aldsworth in 1793 by Sir James Dutton who became Baron Sherborne in 1784.

The effect of these enclosures was enormous and produced greater change in the country than anything for hundreds of years. Half the population of the country was engaged in agriculture. Small yeomen and cottagers would work two or three days for a larger neighbour and the rest of the time on their own account in the open fields and with livestock on the commons.

The yeoman looked upon himself as an equal of his larger neighbour, had often lived in the farmhouse as a young man and was probably a relation and his children married his larger neighbours children. For centuries these smallholders had been skilled in the raising of crops and livestock but never in the handling of money. The larger farmers had been slowly acquiring this ability.

When enclosure came all those who lost their common rights were compensated with money and since there was nowhere to keep stock, they sold what animals they had. They frequently spent the money and went to work for wages for their larger neighbours. Some went to the towns. But they lost their rights and the way of life they and their forbears had always followed.

The landowners on the other hand benefited enormously as did the large tenant farmers from the greatly increased production and consequently the rise in the value of land and rents.

After enclosure in Aldsworth, production increased from ten cattle and two hundred sheep to twenty cattle and eighteen hundred sheep. Grain yield went up from seven hundred and twenty quarters (one hundred and sixty-two tons) to two thousand three hundred and sixty quarters (five hundred and thirty-one tons).

James Dutton was a fairly enlightened landlord who attempted to alleviate the hardship caused by the enclosure by building twenty cottages in Aldsworth with a rood of land (¼ acre) each to be let at thirty shillings a year.

To start with there was work for all, as new farms had to have new walls built round every field; new roads were surveyed, running in a straight line with the church, the focal point. These roads all had to be stoned and walls built along their whole length. The stones had to be hauled with carts and oxen from nearby quarries and off the fields.

The population of Aldsworth in 1700 was one hundred and twenty and there were fifty-four houses. By 1800 the population had risen to two hundred and eighty-eight, part of the rise no doubt being due to the Bibury races.

The Racecourse

Although remote this part of the country was well known and had been since the time of Charles II. This was due to the racecourse which had been laid out on the Upton Downs towards Burford in 1663 and which had then moved on to the Aldsworth land in the seventeenth century. The fashionable "Bibury Club" was founded in 1798, which brought a certain amount of prosperity to the district.

Due to the enclosures of 1793 and the building of walls the racecourse had to be altered in 1801 when a new grandstand was built, but the course remained on Ladbarrow Farm. Horses were stabled in Aldsworth village and looked after the whole year round by grooms and trainers.

Wall Farm

To this newly enclosed village of Aldsworth came in 1799 two Garne brothers, William, the elder by ten years and John. The reason for this move is not difficult to guess. James Dutton, Lord Sherborne, had recently enclosed the main farms of the parish and was asking much higher rents and looking for stability in a time of great uncertainty in the country. The French Revolution was raging, there was widespread poverty and change. What more natural that he should turn to an old farming family of his own estate to take over two of the main farms of this parish?

Wall Farm although not one of the larger farms was the oldest, having been occupied as a farmstead by a family called "Wall" in the twelfth century. There was a farmhouse, buildings and about two hundred and eighty acres which had been bought by James Dutton in 1785. This is where William aged fifty-six and his family came in 1799 to found a line which is still in the parish to this day (1983).

William who moved to Wall Farm was undoubtedly a very able and successful farmer. He had been born at Lower Farm, Sherborne, the second son of Thomas Garne and Miriam Wheeler. It is probable he had taken the tenancy of Leygore Farm in the parish of Turkdean two miles west of Northleach sometime before 1775.

At that time the Reverend Henry Hastings farmed the Rectory Farm, Turkdean but he was not the Vicar of Turkdean. His brother was Reverend Pennistone Hastings, Vicar of Bledington, near Stow-on-the-Wold, who had a son, Warren, later to become Governor General of India. On Christmas Eve 1775 William Garne married Reverend Henry Hastings's daughter, Bridget, when she was eighteen and he was thirty-two. They had nine children all of whom were baptised in Sherborne Church.

The Hastings Family

The Hastings family of Daylesford Manor, near Stow-on-the-Wold had been a notable one all through history. Sir Myles de Hastings, a Norman knight, had been the first owner of Daylesford in the time of Henry I. Being intensely loyal to the Royal family, John Hastings gave most of the family fortune to the Royalist cause in the civil war, so several generations later in 1715 Reverend Pynaston Hastings was forced to sell Daylesford Manor.

Warren Hastings was born in 1732 and from his earliest years it was his ambition to buy back the family estate. This he achieved in 1788 when he finally returned from India. He bought Daylesford Manor and

Gloucester, Augt. 24th. 1822.

My Dear Sister,

Several years have now elapsed since I last had the pleasure of seeing you, and although living at so easy a distance from each other, I have not since that time heard of your health or anything relating to you, thro' a satisfactory a channel. The last time I seen you, I recollect was occasioned by the death of our Brother Thomas calling me to Cheltenham, when, in the company of Henry, I extended my journey to your house, and this must now be bordering on   years ago; and I have really been extremely anxious for some time, again to journey-up and see you, but as I am situated, the chance of my doing so is, as it were, almost next to impossible; for it would be the greatest difficulty on earth for me to leave my employment for the time it would require to come up and return. — Such being the case, I have hit upon the following expedient to obtain the most satisfactory information of your health, &c: My Son (who is Clerk in the Office of the Gloucester Journal, a copy of which, containing an account of the Assizes, is sent herewith) having some enforcement of this invitation in her hands.

The Family desire their very kind respects to yourself and all belonging to them; and I remain,

My Dear Sister believe me,

Your affectionate Brother,

John Hastings.

Business to do at Cheltenham, on Monday, ~~August~~ Septr 2nd.
I have requested him to take a Gig, give his Mother
a seat, and drive as far as your House, to this, I am
happy to say, he has assented, and, therefore, if nothing
unforeseen happens, they propose paying you a visit sometime in the forenoon of that day, and, I doubt not, but you
will, on my account, be glad to receive them.

Although I have now been married 27 years, you
have never once seen my wife: you will find her
"one after your own heart,"– a plain, decent woman;
clean and industrious, sure criterions of a good wife.
They will stop at your House, if convenient, or else at
Northleach, for one night, and return home the next day,
as their several occupations will not afford them greater
license. Formerly I had now-and then a call from one
of your Sons, I believe William, on his way to some Fair
below Gloucester, but of late years he has not attended
there, and so the means of hearing of you is cut off in a
quarter the best able to furnish it correctly.– I gather,
tho' very seldom, a faint scrap of intelligence from some person
or other whom chance may throw in my way, and this being so
very indefinite is far from allaying my anxiety.

I can furnish you with no intelligence worth ~~commu~~-
communicating respecting Henry & James; I see them very
seldom, the former in particular. Since I seen you last, they
have both been re-married: it is James's third wife! and
she has been represented to me, both by himself and others, as

six hundred and fifty acres for £11,424, but it cost a vast sum to restore. He took a great interest in farming and livestock in his retirement, living the life of a country squire. He was known to be generous to his relatives, so it is not unlikely that he helped his first cousin, Bridget and her husband William Garne when they moved to Aldsworth in 1800; particularly as there are a number of articles which once belonged to Warren Hastings, still in the possession of members of the Garne family and their relations, including his engraved gold ring.

Unfortunately William had only been at Wall Farm two years when he died leaving his widow Bridget and nine children. The eldest, Jane, was twenty-six and the youngest, Jemima was two. Fortunately Bridget had three sons to run the farm, two of whom were to prove to be men of exceptional farming ability. The second son, John we know nothing about except for his death at the age of forty-five in Aldsworth in 1828. Bridget too must have been a woman of character as according to the tithe records and the land tax assessments, she continued as tenant of Wall Farm for the remaining thirty years of her life.

Only two of her six daughters ever married and only the eldest, Jane had any children.

It was the common practice at the time for members of the leading farming families to marry the sons and daughters of neighbouring farming families, usually by special licence which was considered to have certain social advantages. The reading of banns in church was looked upon as for the common people. Transport was the horse and roads were bad. Villages and farms were remote and scattered so the scope for finding a bride or husband was very limited. Although marriages were not arranged they came close to it. The material advantages of uniting the main farming families of the district were accepted by all concerned.

Unfortunately the main drawback was the resultant in-breeding. Marriages of cousins were fairly common. This produced people very much of the same type and similar in character. In the case of the Garnes they were physically strong and good looking. Occasionally though there were those of weak mentality.

It was the aim of most large farmers to see their sons settled as tenants of farms in the district. It was also in the interest of most landowners and large estates to let farms to the sons of their best tenant farmers, who usually had the capital and ability to farm the land profitably and so pay a good rent and improve the farm. In each succeeding generation on the Sherborne estate members of the Garne family were the tenants. This went on for nearly three hundred years.

In this early nineteenth century generation the two sons of William and Bridget both moved to other Sherborne estate farms, married, brought up large families, who carried on Garne farming traditions.

Ladbarrow Farm

Ladbarrow Farm of about six hundred acres is away to the east of the parish and in 1799 had a small farmhouse and a stone barn built in 1795 after enclosure.

This is where John Garne and his family came in 1800. Two years earlier John's wife Minerva Larner had died leaving him with three daughters and a son. The two elder daughters married from Ladbarrow. Jane married Thomas Houlton who was head gamekeeper on the Sherborne estate in 1806 and Jemima married Edmund Stone of Aldsworth in 1813. He was a small farmer at the time and later became the village shoemaker, another of those who lost out on the enclosure of the parish. His son, John Stone later on worked at Ladbarrow for his mother's brother Thomas Garne.

The third daughter, Mary never married but presumably kept house for her father and brother.

Thomas was the only son, who took over the farm on his father's death in 1823. He did not marry until he was forty-six in 1830 to Lucy Waine, probably the daughter of Joseph and Mary Waine, since they were the witnesses at the wedding in Aldsworth. Lucy was thirty-four and unfortunately they had no children.

The Waine family had owned the Green Farm of two hundred acres since 1766. They were the only family to own land in the parish other then the Lord of the Manor, Lord Sherborne.

It seems probable that one of the disadvantages of Ladbarrow Farm was the racecourse owned by the fashionable Bibury Club which attracted people from all over the country, including many of the wealthy and idle. The Prince of Wales attended a four day summer meeting in 1802. Although the club declined after 1814 there remained a racecourse until Thomas Garne's death in 1851. It is known that Thomas Garne disapproved of the racing, probably due to the damage done to his crops and stock by the huge crowds against whom he had no redress. There were paths to the course across his fields which in the summer were standing corn. To discourage the use of these paths particularly by ladies in crinolines Thomas used to sprinkle red raddle powder, used in sheep farming, on the stalks of corn.

The parson of the parish was also opposed to the racing, largely due to the undesirable people it encouraged and the amount of drunkeness and riotous behaviour resulting.

Thomas was not known for showing sheep or cattle and it is more than likely that he and his family did not get on with William Garne and his family at Blackpitts. I base this supposition on the fact that both Thomas and his father, John, were buried at Sherborne and not at Aldsworth and Thomas's wife, Lucy, was buried at Aldsworth in a different part of the churchyard to the other Garnes. Moreover eighty years later the descendants of William Garne said they were in no way related to the Garnes of Ladbarrow. This was probably due to the prevalence of snobbery in Victorian and Edwardian England when it was common for members of a family to disown other members for reasons of imagined superiority or from a long forgotten quarrel.

On Thomas Garne's death in 1851 the tenancy of Ladbarrow passed to Thomas Houlton, a nephew. He was the second son of Jane Garne and Thomas Houlton, the gamekeeper. Thirty years later it passed to John Houlton, a son of Thomas Houlton. After a short break the tenancy went to Tom Garne in 1912, a descendant of William Garne of Blackpitts. Tom and his son, Robert, remained until 1936 when the farm was sold by James Dutton, Lord Sherborne, to Mr. Maurice Willes who still farms it (1983). So apart from a short period when George Hewer was tenant, John Garne's descendants occupied Ladbarrow Farm for one hundred and thirty-six years.

CHAPTER IV

Two Famous Farmers

William of Aldsworth 1781-1857

This William was the first member of the Garne family to put the Garnes in the forefront of British farmers. Although his father, William, had moved to Aldsworth in 1800 he only lived two more years so it fell to his eldest son, who was twenty-one at the time, to run Wall Farm for his mother with the help of his two brothers, John and Thomas.

In 1809 he married Marianne Waine of the Green Farm, Aldsworth. A sampler she worked at the age of fourteen dated 30th April, 1803 is now in the possession of William Garne of Meysey Hampton, his great-great-grandson. They had nine children.

The period in which William and Marianne lived was one of great change. The French Revolution, the Napoleonic wars and the enclosure of the land had resulted in the collapse of rural prosperity. The passing of the yeoman farmer had left a gap not really filled by the tenant farmer.

When William was born in the eighteenth century life in an English village and farming was carried on much as it had been for centuries. The common fields in strips were ploughed by oxen. Sheep and a few cattle grazed on the commons or the stubble after harvest and the meadows after haymaking. The farm labourers lived and ate in the farmhouse with the farmer and his family. Often they were his relations. Few in the village could read or write except perhaps the squire and the parson, one or two large farmers and the clerk.

When William died in 1857 the country and the village was an entirely different place. It was a period of agricultural prosperity. The fears of riot and revolution had passed. The period of acute poverty and near starvation for the poor at the beginning of the century had passed. A great gap had formed between the farmer and his family on the one hand and the labourers on the other. They were now on quite different social planes.

A farmer of ability such as William Garne was, who was fortunate enough to obtain the tenancy of a large farm at the beginning of the century could not fail to grow wealthy by the middle of the century. Everything favoured the tenant farmer and the landlord.

The first advantage of William Garne's position was his ability to produce an enormous increase on a newly enclosed farm. The second advantage was the tremendous rise in prices due to scarcity and the French war. The corn laws had been introduced in 1815 by parliament, most of whose members were country landowners, putting a tax on imported grain. For five of the first thirteen years of the century wheat fetched the high price of £5 a quarter (2¼ cwt) and bread was 1/3d for a 4lb loaf. The third advantage was the enormous supply of cheap labour. Half the population of the country was engaged in agriculture. This was almost the only employment in remote villages. Wages were nominally 7/- a week, but there was no requirement to pay wages for wet days or when there was not much work or during illness. So there was vast unemployment. The system of parish relief was such that the parish rate supported those unable to earn enough to live on. This meant farmers kept wages down and paid as little as possible. A fifth of the rural population was on parish relief in 1815.

It is quite impossible to say after this length of time how William Garne conducted his business or what was his character but there is no doubt he was materially successful as you would expect, given the conditions obtaining as outlined above. There is no reason to suppose he acted or lived in any way different from numbers of other tenant farmers of the period.

* * *

Aldsworth Church was held in plurality with Turkdean from 1736 to 1837 and was styled a perpetual curacy. There was therefore no resident incumbent, but the parson of Turkdean rode his horse over for Sunday services sometimes. In a time of poor communications the system was for the verger to watch from Aldsworth tower for a sight of the parson on his horse at the top of Larket Hill two miles to the west on a Sunday. Only then would he ring the bell for the congregation to assemble. If he did not ring there was no service.

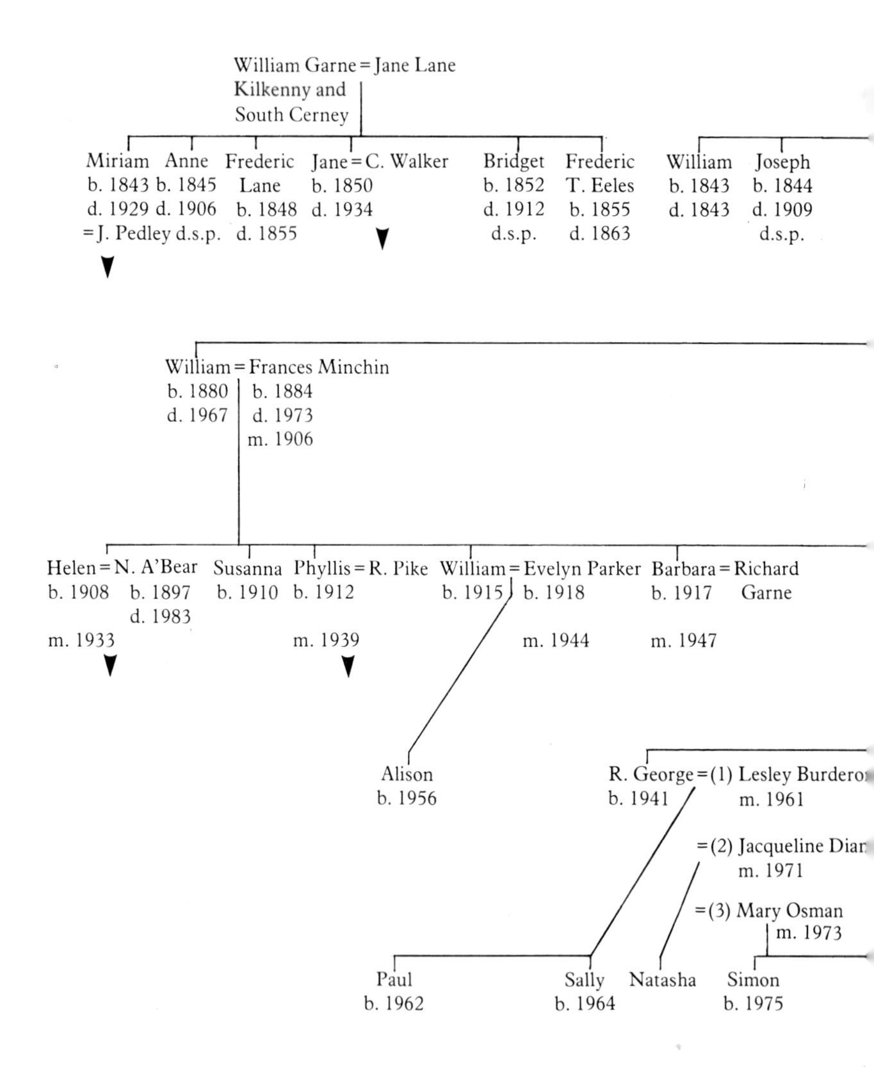
William Garne = Jane Lane
Kilkenny and
South Cerney
Miriam
b. 1843
d. 1929
= J. Pedley
Anne
b. 1845
d. 1906
d.s.p.
Frederic
Lane
b. 1848
d. 1855
Jane = C. Walker
b. 1850
d. 1934
Bridget
b. 1852
d. 1912
d.s.p.
Frederic
T. Eeles
b. 1855
d. 1863
William
b. 1843
d. 1843
Joseph
b. 1844
d. 1909
d.s.p.
William = Frances Minchin
b. 1880
d. 1967
b. 1884
d. 1973
m. 1906
Helen = N. A'Bear
b. 1908
b. 1897
d. 1983
m. 1933
Susanna
b. 1910
Phyllis = R. Pike
b. 1912
m. 1939
William = Evelyn Parker
b. 1915
b. 1918
m. 1944
Barbara = Richard
b. 1917
Garne
m. 1947
Alison
b. 1956
R. George = (1) Lesley Burderoı
b. 1941
m. 1961
= (2) Jacqueline Diar
m. 1971
= (3) Mary Osman
m. 1973
Paul
b. 1962
Sally
b. 1964
Natasha
Simon
b. 1975

THE ALDSWORTH BRANCH 1843-1984

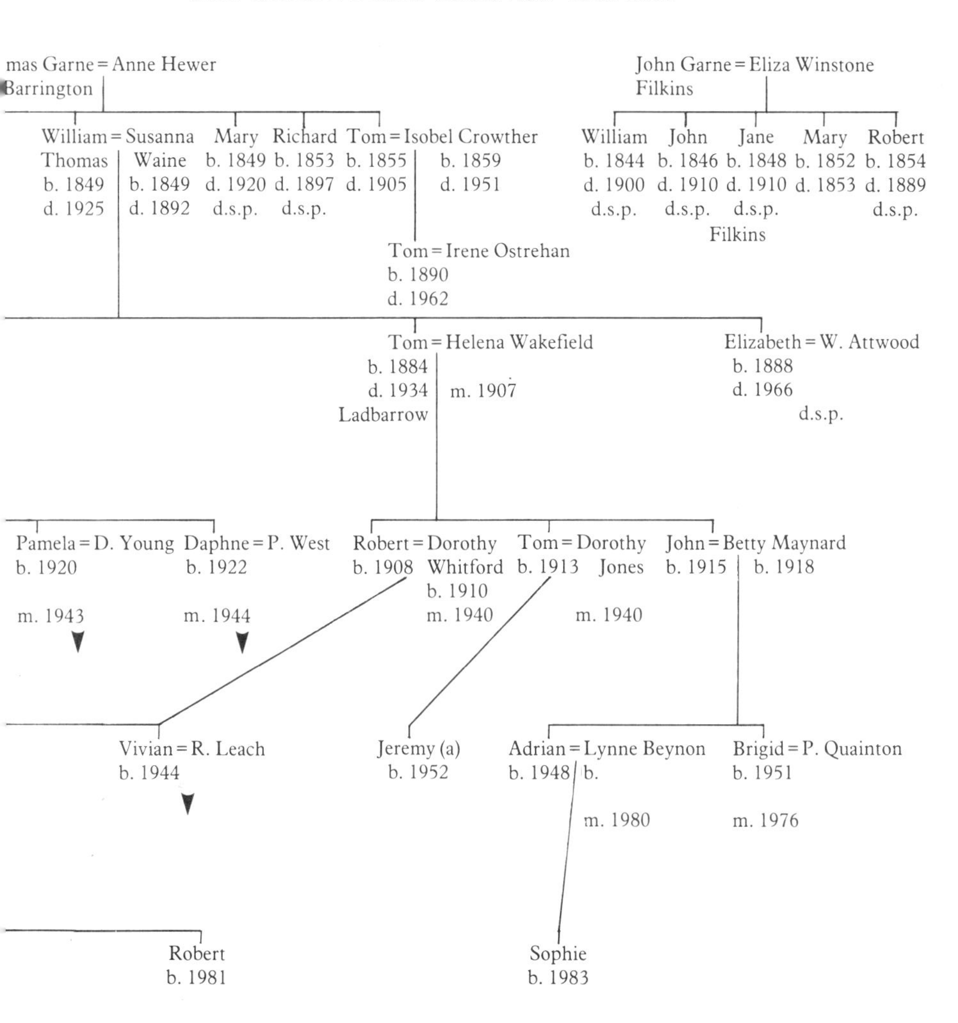

There was thus only one churchwarden, William Garne. The position was an important one before the days of parish councils and local government. He was responsible for roads, bridges, floods and administering and collecting the poor rate. This latter usually with the help of an overseer of the poor, but sometimes the same man. In a parish such as Aldsworth with no resident squire or vicar, the churchwarden was leader of the village.

The cost of relief in Aldsworth in 1813 rose to £294 with twenty-nine people on occasional aid. The work was taken over in 1836 by the Northleach poor law union with its unpopular workhouse.

Quite early in the century, probably 1818, William took over the tenancy of Smith's Farm, also owned by Lord Sherborne while his brothers, John and Thomas, continued to run Wall Farm with their mother, Bridget. The Smith family had been yeomen in Aldsworth for a long time and were a family who suffered from the enclosures of 1793. Lawrence Smith was the last of the line who gave up about this time. It is possible that William and Marianne lived in the Smith's farmhouse when the Smiths moved out after 1815. A century later this house was occupied by the herdsman, Albert Forsyth. The name Smith's yard was retained until 1967.

In 1831 four farmers in Aldsworth employed seventy labourers.

In 1839 the Sherborne estate was organised into six farms in Aldsworth. They were Cocklebarrow, eight hundred and seven acres; Ladbarrow, five hundred and ninety-one acres; Blackpitts, five hundred and seventy-five acres; Wall, four hundred and seventy-seven acres and Conygree, one hundred and forty-six acres.

Smiths Farm had disappeared and was now called New Blackpitts with William Garne as tenant. His mother, Bridget, had died in 1832 and so William was farming one thousand and fifty-four acres, but it is not known whether he lived in Wall Farmhouse, Smith's Farmhouse or a house on the site of the present Blackpitts Farmhouse. When he was first married William was paying rates for a house separate from Wall Farm. Tradition in Aldsworth has it that the present Blackpitts Farmhouse was built for William's youngest son, Robert, in 1854 in William's lifetime using local stone and local labour. Much of the stone came from demolishing older houses then standing in what is now the vegetable garden of Blackpitts house. Plainly William and his son, Robert, were on very good terms with their landlord, Lord Sherborne to build a substantial farmhouse at their own expense. Although one would assume that this would be reflected in the rent. The lease granted to Robert Garne in 1858 after his father's death was for fourteen years at a rent of £1,200 per year for the thousand and fifty-four acres. During this period the landlord was doing very well. Some local land was sold for £150 an acre. Nearly a century later in 1940 the price had dropped to £20 an acre.

The main livestock on the farm was still the Cotswold sheep flock which increased in numbers and profitability. In 1830 there was a severe outbreak of "Rot" in sheep all over the country in which two million sheep died. This is now known as "liverfluke" transmitted by snails in wet seasons. The Cotswold hills would have been ideally healthy and probably free of this disease so there is no evidence that the Aldsworth flock was affected.

In the Gloucester Journal of 6th June, 1829 priced at 7d there is an advertisement which states:— At Aldsworth, Northleach, Glos. "William Garne begs leave to inform his friends and the public that he will offer his TUPS for LETTING, on Tuesday the 16th June, when he will be happy to see any Gentleman who will favour him with their company, or on any succeeding Tuesdays or Fridays during the season". Aldsworth, 27th May, 1829.

The practice of "letting" rams instead of selling them had been started by Robert Bakewell the famous Leicestershire animal breeder fifty years before. It had the advantage for the breeder of being able to go on using proven rams.

The sheep were a necessary part of the farming system at this time to maintain fertility to grow corn before the introduction of artificial fertilizers. The nation was still dependent on home grown wheat to feed the vastly increasing population so corn growing was profitable.

The term "Golden hoof" was often used at this time. There were drawbacks to the system of course, one being the high proportion of clay in Cotswold limestone causing the mud to cake on the sheep's wool in winter when they were folded on roots, of which two hundred acres were grown each year on Blackpitts Farm. This was the system whereby the sheep were given a fresh piece of the crop each day and kept in with hurdles.

In 1839 the Royal Agricultural Society of England was founded and a show was held at Oxford. As a leading sheep breeder William started showing at the Royal Show at York in 1848 which was made possible by the building of the railways. After that he only showed once a year at

Jane Lane (née Garne) 1776-1875. Photo taken in her 100th year.

the Royal Show in a different county each year. He took first prizes for long woolled sheep in 1849, 1850, 1851 and 1852 at Norwich, Exeter, Windsor and Lewes.

William was the first of the family to export sheep. He sent the first batch to the United States of America by sailing ship in 1832. Cotswold sheep were to become one of the main breeds of America.

The flock was doing so well that in 1844 he started holding annual sheep sales on the farm, a practice which continued for over fifty years on Blackpitts Farm.

William also employed a well known artist, W. H. Davis, to come to the farm from London to produce oil paintings of his best sheep. The cover picture is a photograph of one of these owned by the author and his wife, a great-great-granddaughter of William and Marianne.

In the period 1809 until 1830 William and Marianne produced nine children and reared them all, six sons and three daughters. These will appear in a later chapter.

* * *

At about this time (1809) the wife of Henry Lane, who farmed Broadfield Farm, Aldsworth died. She was born Sarah Eeles, a member of a Cotswold farming family. She had three children, one son, Robert Lane who later became famous as a Cotswold sheep breeder at Cottage Farm, Eastington. The same farm now known as Crickley Barrow is once more famous, being owned by Oscar Colburn well known as a sheep and cattle breeder.

Sarah Lane's daughter, Jane, later married William Garne, the eldest son of William and Marianne.

On the death of Sarah Lane, Henry married Jane Garne, the eldest sister of William Garne of Blackpitts. She is notable for the fact that she lived to be just on one hundred. Although she was thirty-eight when she married she had three children, the eldest, William Lane, became famous as a sheep breeder at Broadfield Farm. One daughter, Bridget, married Thomas Houlton of Ladbarrow Farm but unfortunately died aged thirty-one but having had two sons. The other daughter, Sarah Susannah married Richard Waine of Great Barrington. One of their daughters, Susannah, was later to marry William Garne, grandson of William Garne of Blackpitts.

Bridget was the only other one of the five sisters of William Garne of

Wall Farm, Aldsworth.

Ladbarrow Farm, Aldsworth.

Blackpitts to marry. She married Thomas Eeles, the brother of Henry Lane's first wife Bridget Eeles. Thomas Eeles farmed at Cottage Farm, Eastington (later called Crickley Barrow). They had no children and on his death Thomas Eeles left the farm to his nephew, Robert Lane.

The other three sisters of William, Miriam, Anne and Jemima died unmarried. Jemima is remembered as having brought up the children of her brother, Thomas.

Thomas of Broadmoor 1791-1873

Thomas was William's youngest brother. William did have a brother, John, two years younger than himself about whom nothing is known apart from the fact that he was baptised at Sherborne in November 1783 and died in 1828 at the age of forty-five, probably still living at Wall Farm, unmarried.

It was the two brothers, William and Thomas, who were the outstanding men of their generation and who are the ancestors of most Garnes alive today.

The census return of 1851 states Thomas was born at Leygore Manor, Turkdean. Thomas's grandfather, Reverend Henry Hastings farmed Rectory Farm, Turkdean and possibly Thomas's father, William Garne, farmed Leygore.

When Thomas was twenty-eight in 1820 he married Mary Gillett, a farmer's daughter from a farm with the extraordinary name of Woeful Lake just over the Aldsworth boundary in Sherborne parish. The Gilletts were a Quaker family, so as the registration of births, deaths and marriages did not come in until 1837 it is difficult to find the Quaker records of Mary Gillett's birth and death. Although she had five children she was not strong and died young. Her children were brought up by her husband Thomas's single sister, Jemima. They lived together at Wall Farm with Thomas's mother, Bridget.

At Lady Day 1825 Thomas became the tenant of Broadmoor Farm, a bleak farm on the north side of Sherborne parish owned by the same landlord, Lord Sherborne. There he remained for the rest of his life.

But whereas his father and elder brother were sheep breeders Thomas is remembered as a cattle breeder and one of those breeders of the early nineteenth century who enormously improved the breeds of this country.

Like most Cotswold farmers he kept Longhorn cattle which were used for beef, milk and as draught oxen. But very quickly he started

Cotswold Rams of 120 years ago. From a painting by G. R. Whitford, dated 1861, in the possession of Mr. William Garne, of Meysey Hampton, Gloucestershire. The central figure is Robert Lane, of Northleach, Gloucestershire.

THE DESCENT OF THOMAS GARNE OF BROADMOOR 1791-1873

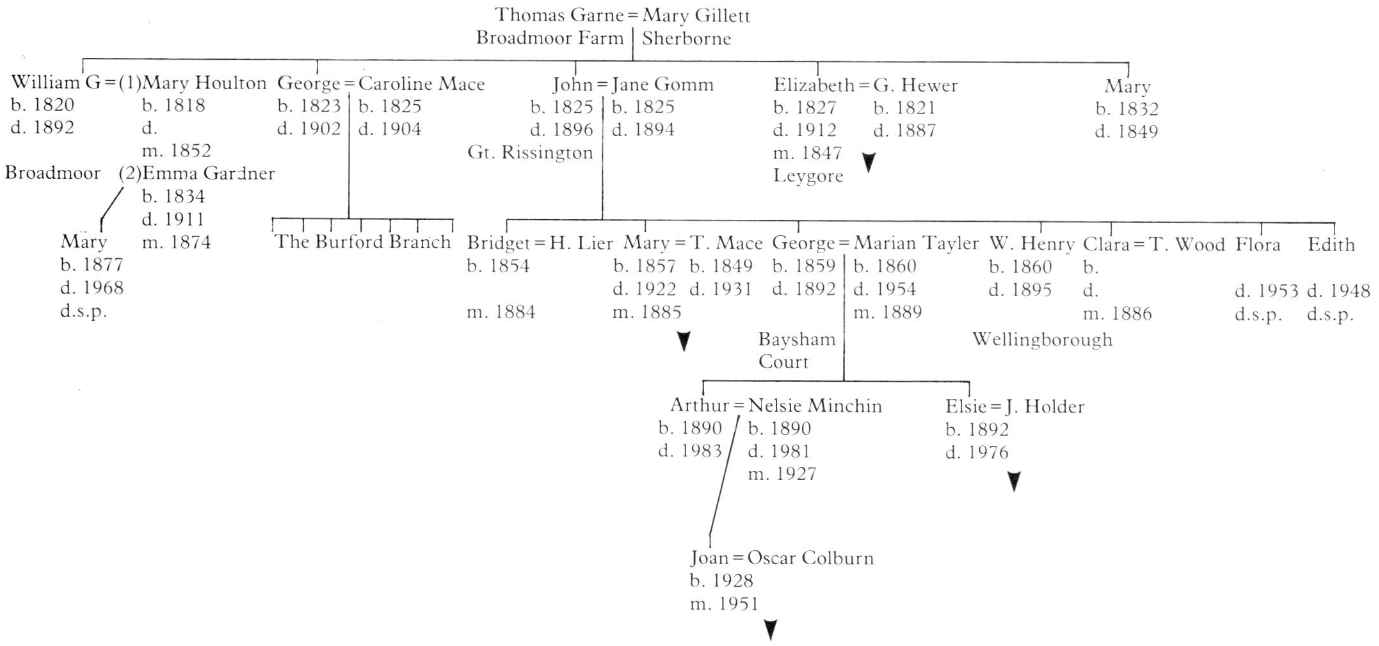

Thomas Garne = Mary Gillett
Broadmoor Farm | Sherborne

William G = (1) Mary Houlton
b. 1820 — b. 1818
d. 1892 — d.
m. 1852
Broadmoor
(2) Emma Gardner
b. 1834
d. 1911
m. 1874

Mary
b. 1877
d. 1968
d.s.p.

George = Caroline Mace
b. 1823 — b. 1825
d. 1902 — d. 1904

The Burford Branch

John = Jane Gomm
b. 1825 — b. 1825
d. 1896 — d. 1894
Gt. Rissington

Bridget = H. Lier
b. 1854
m. 1884

Mary = T. Mace
b. 1857 — b. 1849
d. 1922 — d. 1931
m. 1885

George = Marian Tayler
b. 1859 — b. 1860
d. 1892 — d. 1954
m. 1889
Baysham Court

Arthur = Nelsie Minchin
b. 1890 — b. 1890
d. 1983 — d. 1981
m. 1927

Joan = Oscar Colburn
b. 1928
m. 1951

Elsie = J. Holder
b. 1892
d. 1976

W. Henry
b. 1860
d. 1895

Clara = T. Wood
b.
d.
m. 1886
Wellingborough

Flora
d. 1953
d.s.p.

Edith
d. 1948
d.s.p.

Elizabeth = G. Hewer
b. 1827 — b. 1821
d. 1912 — d. 1887
m. 1847
Leygore

Mary
b. 1832
d. 1849

breeding shorthorns which had just come to the district, by buying cows from Mr. Nathaniel Stilgoe from Oxfordshire and a pure-bred bull from Warwickshire. He also bought from his landlord, John Dutton, Lord Sherborne, a fortnight-old heifer calf called "Pye" for the high price of twenty guineas. This calf, which was from the breeding of Earl Spencer of Northamptonshire, was the founder of a very long line of Shorthorn cattle, which were to remain in the Garne family for the next one hundred and fifty years, by which time it was the oldest pedigree of Shorthorn cattle in England.

For fifty years Thomas Garne of Broadmoor was in the forefront of Shorthorn breeders. He often visited the Booths of Warlaby in the north and bought bulls, but never females as he had fixed a type with his foundation cows, which he was content to improve on.

He only did a limited amount of showing apart from supporting local shows. His herd became so well known he was able to export bulls to Canada and Australia.

On his death in 1873 his herd passed to his three sons, William, George and John. At the dispersal sale breeders came great distances, as by now the herd was famous and the Shorthorn breed was increasing in popularity. It could be said that Shorthorns were also fashionable. Every large landowner had a herd and much study was given to pedigree. Many indifferent animals of the best blood made enormous prices.

In 1874 there was a famous dispersal sale of Shorthorns in New York State, U.S.A. which many English breeders attended where twelve cows averaged £4,000 each. Most of these were of the best English bloodlines. At this time the wage of the herdsman in England was £30 a year.

Large numbers of books have been written on Shorthorn cattle as they were the premier British breed for so long. In 1822 George Coates started his herd book for pedigrees which was taken over by the Shorthorn Society in 1872 and continues to this day.

Thomas is buried in Sherborne New Churchyard under a very large flat tombstone inscribed with only his name and dates.

CHAPTER V

The Cotswolds in Early Victorian Times

All the nine children of William and Marianne Garne were born into Regency England and all except John died in the reign of Queen Victoria, a period of great change in the country and in British farming.

The gentry owned the land, the farmers rented it and the labourers worked. This was the usual pattern in the nineteenth century. There was now a separation between ownership and cultivation. The more profitable farming became the more eager the rich were to buy and the poor to sell. There came about a new class of large tenant farmers who were capitalists running profitable businesses. Numbers of the old small-holders and small yeomen were forced into the towns to pick up what livelihood they could and some of these were successful in other occupations.

This makes a big problem for the genealogist as it is difficult to trace where members of a family moved.

It is probable that the ancestors of Spencer Garne of Western Australia for instance could be traced back to Thomas Garne born in Sherborne in 1756.

This remote corner of Gloucestershire was little different in the day to day affairs of the people than most of southern England. The gap between rich and poor was growing wider the whole time; the gap between farmer and labourer likewise.

Country squires, many of whom had acquired titles, laid out grand parks and built themselves great mansions, employed large numbers of servants and lived in an altogether different style of life from their forebears and completely separate from all the other people living in the villages.

James Dutton had been made a Baron in 1784. His son John in 1830 pulled down the old Sherborne Grange which had been there for centuries, and built an enormous mansion in the Italianate style called

Sherborne Park. But not content with that he also pulled down the old Norman village church and erected a new church joined onto his mansion with a private door linking the two. It looks as if the estate masons did not waste all the church stone however, as there is still a cottage in Sherborne with a beautiful Norman doorway. Over the next fifty years the Duttons rebuilt practically all the village of Sherborne and much of Aldsworth.

At the other end of the scale was the labourer and his family living in desperate poverty, always living from day to day, literally from hand to mouth on the verge of starvation in little better than huts owning practically nothing.

Infant mortality was high and expectation of life low. There was fear and repression on all sides with brutal and savage sentences meted out for the slightest misdemeanors. This was particularly so with regard to poaching which was punished with the utmost severity. Every district had its gallows. Hangman's Stone one mile from Northleach is still a landmark, as gibbets were usually erected on the highroad in a conspicuous place, so that the corpse, left hanging in chains, was a warning to others.

There were no prisons except for a few in London so the usual punishment was transportation to the Colonies; firstly America until independence made that impossible, then Van Dieman's land (later called Tasmania) and Australia. This did not stop until 1846 and public hangings went on until 1868.

Although there was a plentiful supply of labour, both men and women, landowners and large farmers were quick to take advantage of new labour saving machinery being invented. A simple form of threshing machine driven by horsepower was becoming available which did away with the main winter work of the labourer, flail threshing.

It was not surprising that in 1830 there was widespread rioting all over the arable farming counties of England, but excluding the north of England where conditions were quite different.

These riots were known as "Captain Swing" riots after the name of the Wiltshire ringleader (probably a fictitious name). The target of the riots was largely the new threshing machines which were smashed, ricks were fired and damage done to property. But very little violence was directed against people. Strangely enough the chief rioters were not the starving labourers but the more intelligent independent craftsmen who were fighting against injustice.

The riots lasted about six months and were eventually put down with extreme severity using troops. The ringleaders were hanged and large numbers deported in chains to Van Dieman's land and Australia. When the figures were published Sherborne and Aldsworth parishes appeared to have less trouble than in many parishes, possibly due to all the building going on in Sherborne and the racehorse stables in Aldsworth providing some employment.

As in most families the nine children of William and Marianne had much in common. They followed the same occupations and had the same outlook and way of life as most others of their class in early Victorian England. The middle class aim was to "get on", improve and move up in society. Respectability was the main virtue usually linked with outward religious forms essentially of the Church of England.

Large farmers were not usually men of culture or broad views. They did not interest themselves much in national affairs and always voted as their landlords directed which for the Garnes was Tory. Literacy was never held in high regard in rural areas and book learning was rather scorned. Skills in animal breeding and agriculture were passed on by word of mouth from father to son, so sons were always instilled with the sense of following father on the farm and marrying a farmer's daughter. This had been the tradition for centuries.

The main amusements for large farmers were field sports, mainly fox and hare hunting. Shooting was largely the prerogative of the landlord. Comfort and plenty were the standards achieved.

* * *

The eldest child born at Wall Farm was *Elizabeth* known as Betsy, who never married and lived in Aldsworth all her life, the mainstay of the Blackpitts farmhouse after it was rebuilt in 1854 when she was housekeeper for her single brother Robert. She was tall, dark and a dominant character. She was born three months after her parents marriage, a common occurrence.

The next daughter was *Jane,* seven years younger, born with a deformed leg. She too lived and died in Aldsworth also with her sister Betsy and brother Robert.

The youngest of the family was *Bridget* presumably named after her grandmother Bridget Hastings who was still alive. Bridget was the baby of the family, twenty-one years younger than her eldest sister Betsy.

There had always been a story passed down through her family that she died tragically on her wedding eve. This could easily be true but the only report of her death is that appearing in the "Wiltshire and Gloucestershire Standard" of January 1853 which states that she died after a long illness patiently borne aged 23. History does not relate to whom she was engaged, even if this story is true. T.B. was a common disease at the time particularly amongst the young.

Calamity at Kilkenny

William was the eldest of the six sons of William and Marianne of Blackpitts. He was born in 1810 in Aldsworth probably at Wall Farm although this is uncertain.

By the time he was thirty William took the tenancy of neighbouring Kilkenny Farm, 740 acres; indicating that his father must have been doing well to set him up. This farm is just over the Aldsworth parish boundary in the parish of Bibury, although owned at the time by the Duttons of Sherborne. It had been called New Farm when it was first

Kilkenny Farm.

enclosed but the name was changed to Kilkenny after the town in Ireland captured by Cromwell in 1650. It was common for Tory landlords to name farms and fields after national victories and Whig landlords after defeats.

William Garne married on 13th February, 1843 Jane Lane, the only daughter of Henry Lane of Broadfield Farm, another large farm over the Aldsworth boundary to the north.

As Jane Lane was thirty when she married William Garne they only had six children, fewer than the average for the period in which they lived. Since large farmers at that time had plenty of everything and lived in comfort, infant mortality was quite small compared to that of the labourers, who lived in extreme poverty (and infant mortality was very high).

Nevertheless they had their share of misfortune. Their third child was a boy *Frederic Lane* born January 1848, the eldest son of the eldest son and made much of. As was common on large farms beer was home brewed and into a vat of beer young Fred fell head first when nearly eight years old and was drowned.

Two more baby girls followed and finally another boy was born when Jane was forty-two. He was named *Frederic Thomas Eeles.* Thomas had been a Garne name for centuries and Jane's mother was an Eeles. At least there was now a son to carry on after four girls. But misfortune was to strike again. In the harvest of 1863 when the men had gone to dinner leaving their "prongs" (the local name for pitchfork) standing against the rick prongs uppermost, young Fred aged eight slid down the rick and was pierced through and died.

The two brothers both called Fred, both of whom died in September at the age of eight are buried side by side in Aldsworth churchyard under a yew tree.

Surely in a more superstitious age such a tragedy in one family would have been looked upon as evidence of the wrath of Heaven for some misdoing.

Of the daughters the eldest was *Miriam,* tall and dark like her Aunt Betsy. She married Jo Pedley a farmer's son. They had a son Garne Pedley and several daughters, two married local farmers Bertie Edmonds of Meysey Hampton and Will Stevens of Ranbury. Joe Pedley took over Kilkenny Farm when William and Jane moved out in 1867, a move probably brought about by the tragic death of their two sons.

The move was to South Cerney Manor, a much smaller farm than Kilkenny but a large manor house in the village of South Cerney next the the church three miles to the west of Cirencester and about fifteen miles from Aldsworth. Here they lived in some style with their two single daughters *Ann* and *Bridget*. Both these daughters lived with their parents their whole lives and remained in the house after the death of their father when he was eighty-six in 1896. They both lived to about sixty, so South Cerney Manor was occupied by this family for forty-four years.

Daughters born into middle class homes at this period were at a great disadvantage if they never married. There were so few "respectable" occupations they could go in for. Many became governesses; some helped to bring up the children of relatives. They paid prolonged visits to relatives but most "work" was denied to them, especially, as in the case of this family there was the constant aim to push upwards in society. It was a typical Victorian household, solid and respectable. When William married he was described as a yeoman. In his will fifty years later he was described as a gentleman.

The last daughter of William and Jane to marry was Jane Kate who married in 1881 Charlie Walker, a son of Thomas Walker who had been a very successful farmer at Stowell Park, now owned by Lord Vestey. He was a very large man and known to his contemporaries as "the King of the Cotswolds". He had retired to a house in South Cerney opposite South Cerney Manor. This son, Charlie, was a solicitor practicing at Bridgend in Wales. Charlie Walker and Jane Kate Garne only had the one child, Charles William Garne Walker born in 1882. This boy joined the Indian Army with a commission when he left school, had a distinguished career all over the world and died at South Cerney aged ninety-two. He had one son Michael later to become Sir Michael Walker, British High Commissioner in India. What became of Charlie Walker is a mystery. His wife Jane returned to her parents home with her baby boy and was referred to as a widow in her father's will dated 1890. She lived to be eighty-five and all her life was spent in South Cerney.

Thomas of Barrington and his sons Richard and Tom

Thomas was the second son born in 1813. Like his brothers William and John the tenancy of a farm was found for him by the time he was thirty, at the village of Baunton just outside Cirencester.

In 1842 he married *Anne Hewer,* daughter of Joseph Hewer of Shrivenham in Wiltshire member of a local farming family. I cannot establish that Thomas and Anne were close relations although Anne might have been related to Thomas's mother, Marianne Waine, but the fact remains that theirs was a most unfortunate family.

It is an odd thing that although William and Marianne had six sons, five of whom were strong and healthy and four lived to old age, they only had two grandsons and two great-grandsons.

The first misfortune about the children of Thomas and Anne was the eldest, William, who died as a baby. Then the next was a son *Joseph,* who was simple. He was never able to do any work but remained in the village of Great Barrington all his life and lived to be sixty-five. His sister *Mary* was the same and never grew up mentally.

There were three other sons, the eldest *William Thomas* stayed frequently with his grandparents at Aldsworth and was himself later to be the only grandson of William and Marianne to have grandsons. Since he was a notable character in this history he will appear in a later chapter.

The next son was *Richard,* known as Dick, who never married and about whom very little is known. He farmed at Broadmoor Farm on the Sherborne estate sometime after 1882 when his cousin William gave up that farm. Richard must have had some good Cotswold sheep as I have a Smithfield Club medal of his, first prize for Cotswold sheep in 1898. He also had a good herd of Shorthorn cattle which was sold after his death in March 1899 by his brother William who had to administer Richard's estate, as he died leaving no will. His herd averaged 45 guineas each for bulls and cows, considered good prices for 1899 although Thomas Garne's Broadmoor herd of Shorthorns had averaged 81 guineas when dispersed in 1873, before the depression. Richard's death ended Garne occupation of Broadmoor Farm after seventy-five years.

It is not clear what Richard died of, but according to his sale catalogue several cows were sold without a pedigree as Richard had been too ill to attend to this for several years. Some notes found in the effects of Caroline Handy, a cousin of Richard states that he died insane, but without more evidence the matter remains a mystery.

I should think the sheep that won the Smithfield medal had probably been entered by Richard's brother William. Richard was forty-six when he died.

Jane Garne (née Lane), 1813-1882.

William Garne, Kilkenny. 1810-1896.

Richard Garne, Broadmoor Farm. 1853-1897.

Thomas Francis Hewer Garne was the youngest of Thomas and Anne's children born in 1855 at Great Barrington, on the Wingfield estate where his father had taken the tenancy of a large farm sometime about 1848. Thomas Francis Hewer Garne probably remained there till his marriage to Isobelle Crowther, the butler's daughter from Barrington Park in about 1888.

Butlers of this period in large country houses were frequently men of ability and education with considerable responsibility. Tom then moved to a farm called Lanhill, near Chippenham in Wiltshire where their only child was born—Christened Tom but against his mother's wishes. She wanted him called Reg and in fact did call him Reg till he left school.

The misfortune of this family was an outbreak of typhoid fever on the

John Garnes Farmhouse, Filkins.

farm in 1905 which the whole family caught and from which the father Tom Francis Hewer Garne died.

Isobelle Crowther the widow, known to the next generation as Aunt Belle moved to Kent and lived to be ninety-two. She had the bearing of a Duchess and always wore a wig.

Thomas Garne farmed at Great Barrington until his death in 1882. He built up a very successful business with a good Shorthorn herd, most of the stock for which he bought from his cousin George Garne of Churchill Heath.

On his death he left £17,000, most of it to his son William Thomas, but £5,000 in trust for the support of his two simple children Joseph and Mary. To get a rough idea of modern values it is necessary to multiply by twenty.

CHAPTER VI

Good Times and Bad

The Brothers John and Robert

John was the third son of William and Marianne born in 1821; if one leaves out a baby John born in 1819 who died at a few months old. As was common practice the same name was used for the next child born.

John was rather rushed into marriage when he was twenty-two, with one of his parents housemaids, Eliza Winstone, a labourer's daughter from Quenington, a nearby village.

Like his brothers he was put into a farm at Great Rissington where his first three children were born. He then moved in 1851 to The Manor Farm, Filkins, seven hundred acres, over the Oxfordshire border. The house to this day is known as Garne's House, John having been there fifty years.

Filkins village became famous a century after John and Eliza went there as the home of the Chancellor of the Exchequer, Sir Stafford Cripps, a member of a well known Cotswold family.

Filkins is about ten miles east of Aldsworth as the crow flies. By great good fortune in 1979 I met George Swinford, a retired stonemason of Filkins, who was ninety-two and remembered John Garne and his family clearly. George Swinford had been a highly skilled stonemason, like his father, grandfather and great-grandfather. He had started work in 1899 with his father at the age of twelve. They used to leave home at 6.00 a.m. to walk the four miles to work. They had half an hour for breakfast, an hour for dinner and half an hour for tea and knocked off at 8.00 p.m. On Saturdays they only worked till 5.00 p.m. in summer and 4.00 p.m. in winter. He worked all his life for Groves of Milton, a local builder's firm who did much stone work on churches and large buildings.

In 1902 W. T. Garne had a number of alterations carried out to his new house in Aldsworth and young George used to walk the ten miles from Filkins to Aldsworth on a Monday morning. He worked on this house all the week, lodging in a cottage; walking back home on a Saturday evening often shooting a rabbit on the way with a catapult. On one occasion he picked up an egg in the rickyard at Aldsworth which when he hatched it out grew into a magnificent game cock. W. T. Garne was famous for his game fowls.

So thanks to George Swinford I have an accurate picture of John Garne and his family living at Broadwell in the closing years of the last century.

John Garne was a typical old English yeoman, stocky, red faced and independent. He was the type from which "John Bull" was drawn. Good to the poor of the parish, always giving liberally. He was a churchwarden, on the Board of Guardians and a life member of the Royal Agricultural Society of England. He went to Oxford market every week by train as he lived only two miles from a small station, to which he went in his gig. This he drove everywhere until he was too old to climb up and then he had a low four wheeler, rather like Queen Victoria.

Latterly he was known as "Dada" Garne but earlier he was often called "pump", a nickname he acquired when he took charge of the local horse-drawn fire engine at a fire in the village. This machine had a hand operated water pump to get the water out of the village pond. John Garne's orders to the crew could be heard all over the village.

Like most of his relations he had a good herd of Shorthorn cattle and a flock of Cotswold sheep with prize cards pinned to the beams of the bull pens in the traditional manner.

Of course like every other arable farmer he was affected by the agricultural depression in the last quarter of the nineteenth century so that the farm went down. He stuck it out till he was nearly eighty and then moved to a small farm at Fulbrook near Burford where he died aged eighty-six.

George Swinford well remembers the scene on a Saturday evening in summer. Wages were paid weekly at 8.00 p.m. in the farmhouse kitchen, half a sovereign for each man with a little more for senior men. The wives and children were waiting in the road to take the money to the village shop to buy food for the week and pay what was owing from the week before. The shops kept open for as long as there were customers and most of the money was spent that evening.

The strange thing about the children of John and Eliza was that none of them married. One daughter, Mary, died as a baby and the youngest son, Robert, died aged thirty-five. William, the eldest, was good with horses and livestock. He spent all his life from the age of seven on the Manor Farm, Filkins, probably overshadowed by his father, a very dominant character. He is remembered by the boys of Filkins for his habit of being in one of the three pubs in the morning, another in the afternoon and the third one in the evening. This meant that they could arrange their rabbit catching on the farm without being caught. Sometimes they would enjoy riding on the enormous rams some of whom would weigh over four hundred-weight. Since he died aged fifty-six he was probably an alcholic.

The next son, known as Young John or Jackie, took over the Manor Farm when his father got too old. Although Jackie never married he had a housekeeper, Miss Checkitts, who used to accompany him in his dog cart on his visits to his relations. Frances Garne as a young bride at Ablington in 1906, recalls the horror she always felt when she saw Jackie driving his gig furiously up the front drive, the worse for drink, shouting lustily in the Cotswold dialect. Then he would chase her round the kitchen table if her husband, Will Garne, was out, declaiming that Miss Checkitts had a face like the back of a horse.

Most of the Garne family at the time were very respectable and very serious and would rather not mention Jackie Garne or admit that he was a relation.

He died at Fulbrook aged sixty-four and is buried with his father in Fulbrook churchyard and the inscription reads "Young John Garne".

Not much is known about *Jane,* the only daughter. As far as we know she spent her whole life in her parent's house, presumably looking after them in their old age. The only thing George Swinford remembers about her is her size. She was enormous, probably weighed twenty stone and seldom went outside the house. The groom was usually required to get her in and out of bed. She died at Fulbrook the same year as her brother, Jackie, aged sixty-one and so ended this branch of the Garne family.

Richard was the fifth son of William and Marianne of Blackpitts, a name which occurs in the Garne family every four generations. He died unmarried when he was twenty-eight, living with his parents at Blackpitts. Two years after his death his elder brother, Thomas, named a son after him.

Robert Garne. 1825-1900.

Robert Garne of Aldsworth

Robert was the youngest and in many ways the best known of the six sons of William and Marianne. He spent his whole life on Blackpitts Farm and never married.

In his early years Robert, being the youngest son, stayed at home and helped his father, so that when the latter died in 1857, Robert was in a strong position to inherit the live and deadstock on the eleven hundred acre farm and carry on the tenancy.

Robert was big and strong, which was not surprising, as for generations he and his forebears had lived on the best food.

He was a dominant character who ruled the village of Aldsworth for most of his life, was held in great respect far and wide and feared by a great many. He was in fact a typical Victorian businessman and employer. Although there was a very serious agricultural depression which particularly affected large arable farmers for the last twenty-five years of Robert's life in which large numbers of arable farmers were forced to give up or go bankrupt, Robert increased his holding and made a fortune.

In 1875 before the depression was really noticed, Robert bought a farm in Ablington, a small village about five miles south. This consisted of two hundred and six acres, a good farmhouse, called at the time "The Cottage" but later known as Hinton House (after a family who farmed there in the eighteenth century) and five stone built cottages, all for £6,600. He let the farmhouse back to James Newman who had once owned the farm. Robert farmed the two hundred and six acres on the traditional system of barley, clover and roots with a foreman living in the best cottage. He still farmed the thousand and fifty four acres in Aldsworth.

Arthur Gibbs in his book "A Cotswold Village" published in 1898 refers to Robert Garne as a Yeoman Prince enjoying a higher standard of life than most squires of the period. Arthur Gibbs lived at Ablington Manor with his parents and paints an accurate picture of life in Ablington at the turn of the century.

In the middle years of the last century Cotswold villages were small units on their own which had little contact with the outside world as in fact they had been for hundreds of years. Aldsworth is eleven miles from Cirencester, always known as the capital of the Cotswolds and four miles from Northleach to the north on the turnpike coach route from London to Cheltenham, Gloucester and the west.

Aldsworth village had its blacksmith, wheelwright, grocer, innkeeper, shoemaker, dressmaker, malster and brewer. Some of these employed extra help and supplied all the necessities of life. For the bulk of the population it was only the barest necessities which could be afforded. A wage of 8/- a week would only buy the simplest food and not enough of that if there were several children. But that was the wage of a farm labourer, a mistaken title in use until the second world war, because in fact most men were highly skilled. Nevertheless they were looked upon as the bottom of the social scale by the rest of the nation. They were badly paid, undernourished, badly housed, overcrowded and worked very long hours, 6.00 a.m. to 8.00 p.m. six days a week. Naturally they were frequently deceitful and dependent on charity. Alternative occupation practically did not exist. Almost all were illiterate and quite unaware of what went on in the rest of the country or the world.

Everyone working on farms lived in a tied cottage controlled by the farmers, usually engaged for a year at a time from Michaelmas, at Cirencester Mop Fair. This was the one day a year a man had off work if he was leaving the farm. Many men went to a different farm each year taking wife, children and all their possessions on a farm wagon hoping that a new farm would be better than the last. Most farmers went to the hiring fair looking for men from whom they could get the most work for the least money. It was looked upon as a virtue among farmers to drive a hard bargain over everything. The only men who had a higher wage and slightly more security were shepherds and herdsmen. The shepherd also enjoyed a higher status.

On most large Cotswold farms the shepherd was the key man. It was he who was responsible for bringing out the shearling rams at the annual sale on the farm on which the whole farm economy depended. The best rams might fetch a hundred guineas or more. The shepherd would expect to receive a purse at these annual sales which might come to £5. Those attending the sale were expected to drop a shilling in the purse.

These annual sheep sales on Blackpitts Farm had been started by Robert's father in 1844 and were carried on for fifty years. People came from all over the district and free hospitality was provided for all. The same thing was carried on by all the leading Cotswold sheep breeders so there was an extensive round of social celebrations. There was great rivalry between the leading breeders as to whose rams would fetch the highest prices. William Lane of Broadfield and Robert Garne of Aldsworth competed against each other to put on the best show.

The coming of the railway had a considerable impact on the whole of rural England. In 1848 Brunel laid the Great Western Railway from London to Cheltenham and the west. Such was the power of Cotswold landowners however that no railway line was laid across the Cotswolds where it might spoil the landscape or the hunting.

By 1858 a single track local line had been built with a station at Fosscross about six miles from Aldsworth. There was also a station at Fairford, eight miles to the south. This made it possible to send Cotswold rams to the annual Royal Agricultural Show which was held at different county towns each year. Robert Garne's sheep were usually among the prizewinners. Coal and guano for fertilizer could also be collected by horse and wagon from the railway station.

I have not been able to find out when Longhorn oxen ceased to be the main motive power on Blackpitts Farm and were replaced by heavy horses but I should think it was a slow change as was almost every change in farming at the time. It might be a hundred years from the time the most progressive farmer started to use a new tool or fresh technique to the time when the old method was no longer used.

The draught oxen, usually Hereford crosses, were often bought at Hereford market by Robert Garne's nephew, W. T. Garne, who had a good eye for cattle and who worked for his uncle as assistant. One year in the seventies he returned saying there were no suitable oxen available so he had bought some Shorthorn cows instead. This started the Aldsworth herd of Shorthorns which was later to achieve national fame.

Throughout this period all over the arable farming districts of England, that is mostly East Anglia and the Southern Counties, the general dissatisfaction with low wages persuaded many farm labourers to band together to try and improve their position.

There were always far too many men in every village and farmers often found it cheaper to employ women and children, so men were stood off every winter in bad weather and were dependent on parish relief or charity to live.

This banding together therefore only met with very limited success until a leader, Joseph Arch, succeeded in forming a union. He was a skilled farm worker who lived in his own cottage and by clever oratory persuaded farm labourers in many areas to strike for higher wages. As a result wages were raised over a wide area. However there was great

Cotswold Ram. 1st prize, Royal Agricultural Society's Show, Warwick, 1892. The property of, and bred by, Mr. Robert Garne, Aldsworth, Northleach, Gloucestershire.
Photo by C. Reid, Wishaw, N.B.

Cotswold Shearling Ram. Shown by Mr. W. Garne, Ablington, Fairford, Gloucestershire—1st Royal Show, Cardiff.

difficulty in holding such a union together and farmers were determined to retaliate. Meetings were held in Gloucestershire at one of which the Bishop of Gloucester said Joseph Arch was a rebel who should be ducked in a horse trough.

Matters came to a head in 1874 when farmers forced a "lock out" for several summer months after the labourers had asked for a rise of 2/- a week from 10/- to 12/- a week. Robert Garne with the help of his nephew, W. T. Garne and John Houlton, the son of the tenant of Ladbarrow Farm fed the livestock and ran the farm. Within a fortnight the labourers were starving and asking for their jobs back. Robert employed over fifty men at the time. No doubt there was no rise in wages but Robert gave his two assistants a gold watch apiece for their support. This ended the one and only wages dispute in Aldsworth in the nineteenth century. From then on it was "That is the wage, take it or leave it". The workers union hardly existed thereafter.

In 1873 Thomas Garne of Broadmoor, Robert's uncle, died. He it was who had founded the Garne herd of Shorthorn cattle. Naturally Robert bought a few animals at the sale and slowly built up a successful herd buying a few more at the sale of George Garne in 1880.

Most of Blackpitts Farm is bleak and cold situated six hundred feet above sea level and with few trees. Being on limestone with no pastures or fertile valleys it was not thought an ideal place to produce a good herd. Nevertheless by growing crops of clover and sainfoin and skilful management a highly successful herd slowly evolved.

About this time Robert acquired another farm, Home Farm, Naunton of two hundred and forty-six acres. This farm about twenty-five miles north of Aldsworth on the River Windrush had been bought in 1857 for £7,542 by William Hanks with money borrowed from William Garne of Kilkenny and Thomas Garne at Barrington at 4½% interest. But at some stage the whole sum appears to have been guaranteed by Robert as it was part of his estate on his death, and let to G. Hanks, who bought it back in 1917 from Robert's nephew W. T. Garne.

In 1885 and 1886 Robert's two sisters died so his nephew, W. T. Garne and his wife and family moved into Blackpitts farmhouse where Robert was looked after by his efficient housekeeper, Miss Miller

The farm had a very able foreman in Mr. Blake, who lived in Wall farmhouse where Robert's grandfather had lived. The story goes that Robert would open his bedroom window in the morning and shout his orders to Mr. Blake at Wall Farm a quarter of a mile away.

Finally cancer of the liver got the better of Robert and he died in August 1900 aged seventy-five. He left a fortune, some £79,000 (nearly two million in today's money) most of it to his nephew, W. T. but he made a long will and left something to almost every one of his relations, but not a penny to any one of his staff who had helped him acquire this fortune.

Long after his death stories were told about Robert Garne and he, more than anyone made the name of Garne well known in farming circles all over the country.

BROADMOOR,

Four miles from Bourton-on-the-Water Station, on the Cheltenham and Chipping Norton Junction Branch of the Great Western Railway.

Important Sale of the Flocks of

400 COTSWOLD & OXFORDSHIRE DOWN

SHEEP,

34 HEAD OF SHORTHORN CATTLE,

18 HORSES,

DONKEY, PIGS, POULTRY, BEES,

Steam Engine and Thrashing Machine, Corn Mill, Elevator, Cattle Float,

AGRICULTURAL IMPLEMENTS,

DAIRY UTENSILS AND EFFECTS,

The property of Mr. William G. Garne, who is relinquishing Farming,

FOR SALE BY AUCTION, BY

ACOCK, HANKS, & GARNE

ON THE PREMISES,

On Wednesday & Thursday, March 22nd & 23rd, 1882.

N.B.—This Stock is being sold in consequence of Mr. Garne leaving Broadmoor. The Sheep will be found in a very healthy state: the COTSWOLDS having been bred on the Farm for a large number of years, Sires of the most noted Blood having been procured regardless of expense. The OXFORDSHIRE DOWNS are descended from the Flocks of Lord Jersey and Messrs. Hunt and Hobbs. The CATTLE are well bred, only pure-bred Bulls having been used. The HORSES powerful and in good working condition. The IMPLEMENTS very useful, and the whole worthy the attention of intending purchasers.

ORDER OF SALE:

Wednesday, March 22nd, at ELEVEN. The Flocks of 400 Cotswold and Oxfordshire Down Sheep, by Acock, Hanks, & Garne; and about 50 Head of pure-bred SHORTHORN CATTLE, by Mr. John Thornton; to commence immediately following One o'clock Luncheon.

Thursday, March 23rd, after ELEVEN o'clock Luncheon. 34 Head of Well-bred Shorthorn Cattle, 18 Horses, Pigs, Poultry, Bees, Agricultural Implements, Dairy Utensils, and Effects, by Acock, Hanks, & Garne.

CLIFT AND STRONG, PRINTERS, STOW-ON-THE-WOLD.

CHAPTER VII

The Children of Broadmoor Farm

We come now to the five children of Thomas Garne who had started farming at Broadmoor in 1825 and his wife Mary Gillett, three of whom were brought up by Thomas's sister, Jemima, at Wall Farm, Aldsworth, the home of his mother. This was because Mary Gillett was not strong and died young.

Mary was the youngest child and died at the age of seventeen.

The other daughter was *Elizabeth* born at Broadmoor Farm, Sherborne in 1827. She married in 1847 George Hewer who had recently inherited from his father Leygore Farm, an eight hundred acre farm at Turkdean, one mile north of Northleach. The Hewers were a well known local farming family connected with the Garnes several times over. Elizabeth and George Hewer remained at Leygore for the rest of their lives and are buried at Turkdean. The remarkable thing about Elizabeth was she had thirteen children, six girls and seven boys and reared them all.

W.G. and the Farming Depression

The eldest son of the family was *William Gillett* Garne or W.G. as he was known. He remained at Broadmoor farming with his father and latterly in partnership with him. In 1852 he married Mary Houlton, daughter of the head gamekeeper at Sherborne Park and sister of Thomas Houlton who farmed Ladbarrow, but they had no children. His father died in 1873 and W.G. organised the highly successful dispersal sale of the Shorthorn herd. The next year he married again, Emma Gardner, a local woman aged forty and they had only one daughter, Mary, who never married. Mary spent most of her life as a governess in Sussex and lived to be ninety-one.

About the year 1875 farming prices fell dramatically, caused by large imports of grain from the American prairies, made possible for the first time by the growing of wheat on virgin land, the building of railways and the development of steamships to bring the grain to England. Large imports of wool from the Colonies had caused the price of wool to fall for several years.

This huge fall in prices had far reaching consequences. Free trade and non interference by government was the policy which was bringing prosperity to the nation, but it was the downfall of the British landed aristocracy and the ruin of thousands of farmers.

On top of this huge fall in prices was the appalling weather of 1878 to 1881. 1879 was cold and wet the whole summer after severe frosts at the end of March. 1879 had the worst weather for a century. It was worse on heavy land but throughout the arable areas of England much grain was never harvested at all. The winter of 1879-80 was long and severe followed by a wet summer in 1880.

There was a severe outbreak of liver fluke in sheep and enormous losses. Sheep numbers declined by four million in the period 1878-82.

Some of the worst hit by this depression were large arable farmers on the Cotswolds. They had lived through what came to be called "the golden age of British farming" enjoying a high standard of life, plenty of cheap labour and servants in the house. Their wives and daughters no longer doing any active work towards the farm or its income. Horses in the stable for hunting and driving. The best of everything and plenty of it. Few kept any accounts so could not see how to meet this sudden disaster. Labour was reduced and rents were not paid. Boys no longer worked on farms at cheap rates but went to school. Thousands of farm labourers went into the towns for work or emigrated to the colonies. In ten years the wheat acreage fell by a hundred thousand. The value of land, livestock and equipment fell steadily. Many farmers went bankrupt and many more were forced to give up farming, among them W. G. Garne.

At Lady Day 1882 there was a two day sale of the live and dead stock at Broadmoor Farm conducted by Acock, Hanks and Garne of Stow-on-the Wold. The next day the Shorthorn herd was dispersed by John Thornton of London. No doubt W.G. was influenced in giving up by the fact that he was sixty-two and he had no son to carry on. He moved to a small farm at Oddington near Stow-on-the-Wold and lived another ten years in retirement and died at Farmington in 1892 leaving £235 in his will. His widow lived another nineteen years.

I have a beautifully written letter of 1836 by William Garne to his father at Broadmoor, written when William was at boarding school at Cirencester aged sixteen.

George Garne, Churchill Heath. 1823-1902.

George and his family

George was the second son of Thomas and Mary of Broadmoor born in 1823. This is the first recorded instance of the name George being given to a Garne boy. In the previous century if boys were named James or Charles after the Stuart Kings, as many Garne boys were, it was usually an indication the parents were Tory supporters and against the Hanoverian King George I. Presumably by 1823 when George Garne was born this prejudice had worn down and we do not see the names James and Charles in the Garne family any more till the twentieth century.

George was born at Wall Farm, Aldsworth at the house of his grandmother, Bridget, two years before his father moved to Broadmoor Farm at Sherborne.

At the age of twenty-four George married Caroline Mace daughter of a farmer, Thomas Mace of Great Rissington, when she was twenty-two. The same year, 1847, his father obtained for him the tenancy of Lower Farm, Eastington, the next parish to Aldsworth towards Northleach.

George and Caroline remained at Eastington eight years and their first four children were born there. Then they moved to Churchill Heath, a farm of five hundred and sixty-one acres near Kingham in Oxfordshire on the estate of Squire Langston. This was a well managed estate where tenant farmers and labourers were both well looked after. Houses, cottages and farm buildings were good and well maintained.

In the next twenty years Churchill Heath became well known all over the country as the home of a famous Shorthorn herd and George Garne made a name for himself as a breeder, having presumably learnt his skill from his father from whom he also obtained his "Rose" and "Pye" cows, the foundation of the herd.

George also had a flock of Cotswold sheep and kept Berkshire pigs which won him many prizes including the championship one year at Birmingham.

George Garne was much respected in the district as a good farmer and a fair and just employer where men remained for long periods. On one occasion one of his men emigrated to New Zealand but did not like it, so George and Squire Langston between them sent the money for his passage home and re-employed him. The man repaid the loan in full slowly by instalments.

The best way to advertise pedigree cattle at the time was by showing them, which George did with marked success all over the country.

Caroline Garne (née Mace). 1825-1904.

Churchill Heath, 1870. George Garnes Shorthorn Cattle.

Churchill Heath was well situated in this respect as Kingham Junction Station was just up the road on the main line from London to Worcester.

In this period George won over sixty major silver trophies and his cattle were in demand all over the country, in the United States, South America and the Colonies. Buyers were continually visiting Churchill Heath so that Squire Langston had a large drawing room built onto the farmhouse where visitors could be entertained. On the walls were oil paintings by well known artists of his Shorthorn cattle and in cabinets were the collection of silver. Fortunately a few of these pictures and silver trophies are still in existence.

According to the census returns of 1871 there were employed on the farm twenty-seven men, seven boys and four women. Today the labour force on the same farm is a farmer and his son with one hundred Shorthorn dairy cows. Shorthorn cattle have been continuously on the farm for one hundred and thirty years.

In the sixties three more children were born to Caroline and George, making three sons and four daughters although unfortunately one daughter, Clara, died as a child of twelve.

Prince Alfred Roan calved Sep 1st 1872
Bred by Messrs Leney & Son Wateringbury
Got by Grand Duke of Kent 26289
dam Princess Alice by British Prince 14197
g. dam Duchess by Duke of Cambridge 12742
g g d Cold Cream by Earl of Dublin 10178
g g g d Pansy by Grey Friar 9172
by Fawsley 6004
by Little John 4232
by Marcellus 2260
by Caliph 1774
by Swing 2721
by Argus 759
by Defender 194
by Petrarch 488
by own Brother to R Collings White Heifer
by Butterfly 104
by Globe 278

George's father Thomas had died in 1873)

Churchill Heath,
Chipping Norton, Oxon.

Jany 29. 1874

Dr Robert

I should have been very much surprised if you had called Prince Alfred anything like a good Bull, but he had had foot & mouth disease & had been badly done besides, still I have confidence in his getting good stock as his Sire is a very first class Bates Bull and his dam is a great good Cow by Booths British Prince, the pedigree you will find over leaf.

Yours truly
G. Garne

Traditionally farmers sons had been educated at the local Grammar schools although most farmers resented spending money on "book learning" and would reduce their children's schooling to the minimum. Girls were never sent to school but gradually with increased prosperity and the desire to be "respectable" and "refined", in large farmhouses governesses were employed. Farmers daughters had little, if anything, to do with farm or dairy work and in fact were discouraged from getting involved, as farming and stockbreeding were not considered desirable or "ladylike" occupations for women.

With the great increase in the number of agricultural books, papers and magazines however, in the middle years of the century, many of the more enlightened farmers began to see the need for a better education for their sons, particularly as almost all Grammar schools had declined sadly.

The old "public" schools only provided a classical education which was of no use to a farmer. There were a few private boarding schools but these were no better. To fill this need there were started proprietory schools to provide a general education suited to middle class needs to fit boys for trade or industry.

These proprietory schools were not private schools run for the profit of the owner but private schools whose purpose was education with independent ideas. They were mainly for boarders but to keep costs down the boys often lived in hostels and ate centrally. Strangely they were later called public schools although essentially private. Framlingham College in Suffolk was one of these schools founded in 1863 particularly for farmers sons, as a memorial to Prince Albert.

George Garne was prosperous by this time so this is where he sent his two younger sons as boarders in 1872. The eldest son, Thomas, was twenty at the time. George Garne's brother, John, also had two sons of the same age so they were sent two years later.

Thomas, the eldest son of George and Caroline, was put in a small farm at Maugersbury near Stow-on-the-Wold when he married in 1876. His wife was Susan Penson, the niece of the neighbouring farmer, Robert Penson of Foxcote. The onset of the agricultural depression was too much for Thomas however and in a few years he gave up and devoted his time to being an auctioneer and valuer with his friend, Robert Hanks, in the firm of Acock, Hanks and Garne of Stow-on-the-Wold. His father having bought Thomas a fifth share in the partnership.

Tom Garne, Maugersbury—Auctioneer. 1852-1898.

Tom Handy, Caroline Handy (née Garne), George Garne, Caroline Garne (née Mace) outside front door of Hampen Farm.

The two elder daughters of George and Caroline were married from Churchill Heath. *Mary* the eldest known as Polly was married in 1869 to a Doctor Edward Cheatle of Revesby in Lincolnshire. They had five children, three sons and two daughters. Strangely enough there was a very well known figure in Burford at the time, Doctor Cheatle, who founded the Cottage Hospital, but I have been unable to trace any relationship with Mary's husband, Doctor Edward Cheatle.

Caroline (Carrie), the second daughter, married in 1874 Tom Handy of Hampen, a farm near Andoversford owned by the Handys since 1802. They had seven children, two sons and five daughters. The eldest son, Tom, was only sixteen when his father died, so his mother carried on the farm in her own name until he was old enough to take over. Tom's son, Robert, still farms Hampen in partnership with his son.

The youngest daughter, *Florence* (Florrie), did not marry till 1890 Frank Lewis of Hereford. They had four children, three boys and a girl.

No doubt the depression and the run of bad seasons due to the weather were the main reasons for George's decision to give up farming, which he did in 1880 when he was fifty seven.

But not to retire, but to found an entirely new business, Garne's brewery at Burford which was to survive until 1967.

It happened that when the two younger sons were due to leave school in 1876 there was the problem of what they should do. Putting them in farms was plainly out of the question.

Willy was sent to Burford, a little country town on the Gloucestershire, Oxfordshire border, to be apprenticed to learn brewing with John Reynolds who owned Burford Brewery. Arthur learnt book-keeping.

Then when George sold up at Churchill Heath he took over Burford Brewery, The Brewery House and three public houses and started trading as George Garne, Brewer, Malster and Hop Merchant. Willy did the brewing, Arthur the books and George managed the business.

The story of Garne's brewery will appear in a later chapter. Sufficient to say here that George and his wife, Caroline, lived until 1902 and 1904 when they were each seventy-nine and are both buried in Burford churchyard.

John and his family

John was the third son of Thomas and Mary born at Broadmoor Farm in 1825. He did not start farming on his own as a young man like

George Garne, Baysham Court. 1859-1892.

most farmer's sons, instead he became a farm manager for Lord Camperdown at Bushey with a herd of Shorthorn cattle.

In 1854 he married Jane Gomm from the Cotswold locality and they had seven children, two sons and five daughters. The tragedy of this family was the death of both sons as young men.

When the agricultural depression began and in the disasterous season of 1879 John started farming on his own account at the age of fifty-four. This had the advantage that ingoing was cheap, prices of everything to do with farming having fallen substantially. He became tenant of a large farm at Great Rissington only two miles across the fields from where he had been born.

He founded what was to become another very successful Garne Shorthorn herd with a few cows from his brother, George's herd at Churchill Heath, which was on the point of being dispersed.

In the next few years three of the daughters of John and Jane were to marry. The eldest, *Bridget,* known as Bessie married Henry Lier, a clerk, and left the district.

The second, daughter, *Mary Jane,* known as Jarie married Tom Mace, a farmer at Fulbrook near Burford. The Mace family had been farmers at Great Rissington for many years.

The third daughter, *Clara,* married in 1886 at Stow Church a man called Tom Wood of London about whom nothing is known.

The two youngest daughters, *Flora* (known as Fully) and *Edith,* did not marry and remained at home. Flora, was her father's favourite and had nothing to do with the farm. Edith on the other hand was very interested in all farming activities and unlike most women of the day took an active part, which in difficult times was no doubt valuable.

The two sons, George and Harry, were sent away to school at Framlingham in Suffolk two years after their cousins, Willy and Arthur.

George was not academically inclined and was taken away after eighteen months as his interest lay in farming. He worked with his father until obtaining the tenancy of a farm, Baysham Court, near Ross-on-Wye. About the same time he married his cousin, Marian Tayler, whose family were brewers and malsters at Northleach and Aldsworth.

They had two children, Arthur born in 1890 and Elsie born in 1892. Then tragically that year on Whit Monday while haymaking near the River Wye, George had a bathe and was drowned, leaving a widow and two babies.

Harry Garne, Wellingborough. 1861-1895.

William Henry or Harry as he was known was sent to Framlingham College the same term as his brother George in 1874 when he was thirteen. He stayed there five years and rose to be captain of the school, cricket captain and football captain. In his last term he was made an assistant master. He then went on to St. John's College, Cambridge where he obtained his B.A. degree in 1883. He was the first Garne ever to go to a university to obtain a degree. It must have cost his father a lot of money when he was just starting farming in the depression.

Harry obtained a post as a maths master at Wellingborough Grammar School in Northamptonshire, a small school which was expanding at the time. His M.A. degree followed in 1886 and in 1888 he gained his L.L.M.

He took an active part in sport, was captain of his college at Cambridge at cricket and football, but did not obtain his "blue". He played frequently for Northamptonshire at football and once in 1883 for Gloucestershire at cricket.

In 1889 he was appointed house master of a newly built house, still known in 1983 as "Garne's House".

Unfortunately in 1893 he caught T.B. which lingered on for two years until he died in May 1895, widely lamented aged only thirty four.

So here was another Garne family where the only two sons died young, but at least in this case one grandson, Arthur, was left to carry on the name.

CHAPTER VIII

Aldsworth in late Victorian Times

W. T. Garne

The practice of brothers giving their children the same christian names generation after generation makes the task of the family historian a very confusing one. As far as possible I have tried to differentiate between those with the same name. The main boys names for a long time had been William and Thomas and now we have a man named William Thomas, known as W.T. for short. During the lifetime of those with the same name confusion was usually avoided by the use of shortenings or nicknames, so we have William, Will, Willy, Bill and Billy and Thomas, Tom and Tommy sometimes all alive at the same time.

W.T. from his earliest youth was the favourite of his bachelor uncle, Robert of Aldsworth, who lived with his two single sisters, Bessie and Jane at Blackpitts after their parents died. The census of 1851 shows that W.T. at the age of five was staying at Blackpitts. His own home at Great Barrington cannot have been a very cheerful place. His eldest brother, William, had died at thirteen weeks, his elder brother, Joseph, was simple as was his only sister, Mary. Two more boys Richard and Tom were born in the next few years, who probably helped their father, Thomas, with the farm.

Robert was concerned for the health of W.T. and so sent him for a long holiday to France in the charge of his friend and neighbour, John Houlton, whose father was tenant of Ladbarrow Farm in Aldsworth.

When he was thirty-three W.T. married his second cousin, Susanna Waine, a daughter of Richard Waine, a tenant farmer of Great Barrington. Susanna was thirty at the time and not very strong. Robert had a house built for them near Blackpitts farmhouse and shortly afterwards took W.T. into partnership. There they lived for the next six years during which time two boys were born, William and Thomas. On

W. T. Garne, Aldsworth. 1846-1925.

Susanna Garne (née Waine), Aldsworth. 1849-1892.

the death of Robert's eldest sister Bessie in 1886, W.T. and his family moved into Blackpitts farmhouse. There a daughter, Bessie was born. This was the last child. One January night in 1892 Susanna was afflicted with appendix trouble, for which at that time there was no relief and no cure, and she died shortly afterwards.

For four years the two men, Robert and his nephew, W.T., the three children and the housekeeper, Miss Miller, lived together. The story goes that Robert thought this an improper state of affairs, so W.T. married Miss Miller in the spring of 1896, discreetly at Chippenham from the house of his brother, Tom.

The Second Farming Depression

The period 1891-99 was the second phase of the great agricultural depression which had begun in the seventies. During this period over two million acres of arable land fell down to grass and weeds without any increase in the livestock population of the country. Farmers were still giving up all over the South of England. There was widespread unemployment. The population of Great Britain had increased in seventy years from sixteen million to forty million. Wages had risen in some trades by 15-20% in fifteen years, but not in farming which still had a national average wage of 14/- per week. There were still very strong links with the past and resistance to change in most agricultural communities.

The system of "Daymen" was still prevalent, whereby a man could be "stood off" at a days notice and only paid by the day.

No real change came about until the Great War reduced the large surplus of farm labourers. As so often in the past, national calamaties improved conditions for those left. Overtime pay and a half day off on Saturdays were introduced in 1914.

The custom of calling the farmer "Master" and his son "Master Will" or "Master Billy" was to last until the Second World War.

By and large farm labourers at this time were badly paid, underfed and dependent on charity as they had been for generations. The number of vagrants and tramps on the roads was considerable. As many as ninety people of both sexes would call at Northleach Prison, used as the "workhouse", each night. There they would get supper, bed and breakfast. After breakfast they had to break up one hundred-weight of hard bath stone into small pieces before going on their way.

This stone was brought by train to Andoversford station and then

Will Garne, Aldsworth. 1880-1967.

Frances Garne (née Minchin), Aldsworth. 1884-1973.

conveyed to Northleach by traction engine. It was used to fill the potholes in the turnpike road and rolled in with a steam roller. The road was mud in winter and white dust in summer.

With these conditions prevailing, long hours for low pay was customary. Stockmen were paid 14/- a week and day men 12/-. The number of men employed was never excessive for the acreage farmed. On Blackpitts Farm there was fourteen men and six boys for one thousand and fifty four acres. On the Green Farm there were six men and a boy for two hundred and ten acres and at Ablington there were six men and a boy for two hundred and eight acres. It was common for the sons of workers to start work on the same farm when they left school and to be paid according to their age with their father's wage. Five shillings a week at age fifteen was customary for a boy who worked with a pair of horses a twelve hour day.

There was practically no other work available for a boy leaving school except what was available in the village, since there was no way of getting anywhere else except on foot.

Most families working on farms were content with very little and took great pride in their work, particularly in their livestock on farms of high standing and reputation such as Blackpitts. Some men would remain for years on the same farm. Everyone had a cottage for which no rent was required and there were large gardens or allotments for all, although an annual rent was required for the allotments by Lord Sherborne's agent.

The payment of wages was a very simple business. W.T.'s eldest son, Will, told me that it was his duty to collect the money from the bank at Northleach four miles away on alternate Friday afternoons. He would ride his horse there and put the money, about £40 in sovereigns, half sovereigns and small change in a little leather bag in his pocket.

Wages were paid fortnightly on a Saturday at 5.00 p.m. usually. The men would line up in the road with the most senior first and the youngest last. The most senior would receive a sovereign and eight shillings for a fortnights work. No deductions were made and Will Garne kept no books. The total was merely shown on the bank statement and sometimes a list was made on a scrap of paper showing what each man received. Very few farmers were interested in records or accounts and most Garnes never wrote more than was absolutely essential.

The Green Farm

In 1897 the Green Farm, Aldsworth which had been owned by the Waine family since 1766 came on the market.

It had been a seperate farm in the village since Tudor times and long before enclosure. The Waines had had a lease of it in 1717 and bought it in 1766. It had passed from father to son ever since. But in 1866 Giles Waine died when his son, John Charles Waine, was only thirteen. One of Giles Waine's daughters, Lucy, had married John Houlton, whose father, Thomas Houlton, was tenant of neighbouring Ladbarrow Farm; so John Houlton took over the running of the Green Farm and lived in the farmhouse.

In the course of time John Houlton's father retired to Fulbrook so John took over the tenancy of Ladbarrow, as well as managing the Green Farm, since the owner, John Charles Waine (known vulgarly in the village as "arse and pockets" from his habit of sitting on the wall with his hands in his pockets) prefered an idle life to the struggle of farming in times of depression. He also resented his brother-in-law, John Houlton. Martha Waine, the widow of Giles Waine still lived in the farmhouse and largely directed what should be done. John Waine had not married and there was no one to carry on the farm. Owing to twenty years of depression this had become very run down. So in March 1897 the land consisting of two hundred and ten acres was put up for sale by auction at the King's Head, Cirencester. It was bought by Sir Michael Hicks-Beach who later became Earl St. Aldwyns of nearby Williamstrip Park at Hatherop. Only the land was sold at this time.

There was a good stone built farmhouse overlooking the village green from which the farm derived its name, as well as a magnificent stone barn and usual range of stone farm buildings, stables, cow-sheds, granary and probably a pair of cottages.

At some stage following the sale of the land of the Green Farm, the whole farm, land and buildings was bought by W.T. The land from Hicks-Beach and the house and buildings from John Waine, who moved to a cottage he bought in Farmington.

The price is not known but in view of the depression and its run down condition it would not have been expensive.

W.T. was a wealthy man even before the death of his Uncle Robert. W.T.'s father, Thomas, had left £17,000 in 1882, most of it to W.T. (Multiply by twenty for todays value) and his share of the partnership of the thirteen hundred acres they were farming must have been considerable.

Following the death of Robert in the summer of 1900, continuity of the farming business was assured as W.T. was a partner. His first action was to give up the tenancy of Wall Farm and Blackpitts which his family had farmed for a hundred years. He had a sale of the pedigree Shorthorns where eighty head averaged £43-1s-2d but he retained the best. The prices realised were only half those of the cattle sold by Thomas Garne of Broadmoor thirty years earlier.

His plan was to concentrate on his main interest, the Shorthorn herd, so to this end he bought some old buildings, originally part of Smiths Farm, from Lord Sherborne, along with Smiths Farmhouse which became the herdsman's house and a few cottages. These buildings along with the newly acquired Green Farm buildings he then restored and altered for the herd. He was not particularly concerned about the appearance of these buildings only their functional efficiency, so quantities of galvanised iron sheets were used for roofing.

Along with the Green Farm of two hundred and ten acres he rented one hundred and twenty acres of the Swyre Farm, in the parish of Aldsworth, belonging to Sir Michael Hicks-Beach. He also kept the Ablington Farm of two hundred and six acres.

The Notgrove Farm which he inherited from his uncle he let to Mr. G. Hanks.

Mrs. Martha Waine continued to live in the Green Farmhouse until her death a few years later when it was occupied by the shepherd, Jim Wilcox, whose father, Tom Wilcox, had been shepherd for Robert Garne. The Wilcoxs, father and son, worked for the Garnes for very nearly a hundred years as shepherds. Jim never married; he devoted so much time to the flock he probably never had time. He occupied the Green Farmhouse with his mother and then his sister and her family until his death in 1953 when he was eighty-one. He practically never retired. He had devoted his entire life to the last remaining flock of Cotswold sheep in England.

Taylers House

On giving up Blackpitts, W.T. naturally had to find another house. It so happened there became available a large Georgian house close to Blackpitts house, which had been owned for some years by the Tayler family who were brewers at Northleach. The house had been altered and improved in 1851 by John Waine who had done well as a malster and brewer. He converted what had been a small farmhouse by putting on a Georgian type facade with sash windows and building an extensive malthouse and cellars for the storage of barrels of beer.

W.T. bought this house from the widow, Mrs. Tayler and immediately altered and modernised it in the latest style with the help of his wife. He put a wing on the house, added a conservatory, moved the front door and put in a handsome oak staircase. He also installed solid fuel central heating, hardly heard of at that time, a bathroom and indoor sanitation. The lighting was by his own acetylene gas plant. He added stables for hunters, a tack room for the groom and a coach house. All the wine from the cellars at Blackpitts had to be conveyed personally by W.T.'s son, Will, with the help of his friend, Dick Houlton. Their attempts to break a bottle by mistake failed as W.T. knew exactly how many bottles there should have been.

The rickyard at Green Farm was converted into a fruit garden and orchard. A brick wall was built topped with glass to protect peaches and nectarines and a gardener employed.

A piece of land opposite the house was rented from Lord Sherborne and converted into a grass tennis court; tennis being a fashionable pursuit at the time among farmers and their families.

To complete this stylish living a motor car was bought for £3,000, the fifth one in Gloucestershire, with registration number AD 5, and a chauffer employed to drive and maintain it. Later the only telephone in the village was installed.

There was no doubt W.T. was very much keeping up with the time and expressing the confidence the nation felt with the new century. Even though, the locals on seeing him being driven on the stony roads in his new car used to say, "There goes old moneybags"!

W.T. depended on his eldest son, Will, to supervise and carry out his orders on this large farming business.

When he was twenty-six in 1906 Will married Frances Minchin who was twenty-two, one of seven daughters of a neighbouring farming family, who had been Cotswold farmers since Tudor times.

At the beginning of the century Will was considered one of the most eligible bachelors at a time when it was common for farmer's sons to marry neighbouring farmer's daughters.

They moved into the Ablington farmhouse and Will lived the life of a sporting farmer of the period, hunting and shooting in the winter with plenty of everything. His wife was busy rearing seven children, six girls and a boy.

Tom Garne, Ladbarrow. 1884-1934.

W.T.'s second son, Tom, was seventeen when great uncle Robert died. He was at school at Wellingborough where his cousin, Harry Garne, had been a housemaster.

Tom was good looking, intelligent and good at games. He was also his father's favourite and with his stepmother he could do no wrong. On leaving Wellingborough he was sent to Jesus College, Cambridge where he was provided with plenty of funds, so that he enjoyed a very extravagant life and gambled away a lot of money. Eventually he was sent down, much to the wrath of his father who considered sending him off to the Colonies. Instead he listened to the advice of his wife and sent him to his brother's farm near Chippenham, where he hoped he would apply himself to work and farming. Unfortunately there was an outbreak of typhoid fever on the farm in 1905 from which Tom's uncle died. Tom was very ill but recovered. On his return to Aldsworth his father obtained for him the tenancy of a small farm at Icomb, near Stow-on-the-Wold where he remained for six years.

In 1907 he married Helena Wakefield, a daughter of Packer Wakefield, a farmer from Signet Hill, near Burford.

W.T.'s daughter, Bessie, was married at about this time to Will Attwood who was learning estate management with Robert Gray, the agent for the Sherborne estate. Will Attwood took the tenancy of Lower Farm, Eastington, the same farm where George Garne had started farming fifty years before.

CHAPTER IX

Burford Brewery

Burford is a little town on the Oxfordshire Gloucestershire border which lies on the main road from London and Oxford to Gloucester and South Wales.

In the early years of the nineteenth century it had been a busy and prosperous little place due to the coaching trade. After the railways were built it declined in population and importance so that by 1900 it was down to twelve hundred people.

In 1798 a man named Street started a small brewery in Sheep Street in what had probably been the brewhouse for the Lamb Inn next door. This brewery was bought by a Mr. Tuckwell in the 1840s, on whose death in 1857, his widow Charlotte Tuckwell of Signet near Burford, had made over the Brewery, the Brewery House, the machinery and equipment and three public houses to her daughter, Isobelle. Isobelle's husband was Thomas Henry Reynolds who with his brother were tenants of the Brewery.

In 1876 George Garne's second son, William George, left Framlingham College when he was rising eighteen. He was sent to Burford to be apprenticed to T. H. Reynolds to learn brewing and to live in his house.

T. H. Reynolds was a leading member of a religious sect called Plymouth Brethren which was enjoying a little popularity at the time in the west country. Willy Garne was at an impressionable age and was converted to these beliefs by T. H. Reynolds and his wife. This fact was to have far reaching consequences in the Garne family for the next seventy years.

The beliefs of Plymouth Brethren were peculiar, mostly based on one sentence from 2 Corinthians 6, "Come out from among them and be ye separate". This was interpreted that members could not eat or drink with "unbelievers" or in fact take part in any activity, not even marriage, with them. Churches and chapels and all who attended them were disapproved of. All games, sports, alcoholic drink, tobacco, theatres and places of entertainment were unacceptable. Even at work members had to keep apart and not consort with others.

What persuaded George Garne to give up farming and take to brewing is not known but no doubt he saw the agricultural depression as something which had come to stay. His eldest son, Thomas, seemed to prefer horse-racing, drinking and living a wild life to hard work. It is probable George saw more future in taking over a country brewery than struggling on in farming. So at Lady Day 1880 he had a dispersal sale of his famous herd of Shorthorn cattle and a separate sale of the live and dead stock of Churchill Heath.

Most landlords were having difficulty in letting arable farms, as tenants first failed on their rents and then gave up or went bankrupt. Squire Langston, like most landlords, had to change his ideas to find a tenant at all. This was the chance for farmers from Wales, Cornwall and Devon to take over Cotswold farms. These men were prepared to work hard with completely different methods to survive. Farmers of large Cotswold farms had always been scornful of dairying and dairy cows, growing vegetables and doing manual work themselves. These newcomers did all these things, kept up no style and did not keep horses or go hunting. One Welsh farmer even kept calves in the drawing room of a Cotswold farm house, so that fifty years later the marks where the manure had stood always showed in damp weather two feet up the wall. Leases had to be rewritten so that there was no longer rigid adherence to rotations, but anything could be grown which did not make a loss. The tenant could also be a non-conformist, hitherto unacceptable by many landlords like Langston.

The Rose family from Cornwall took over Churchill Heath and their descendants had it up until 1982.

So it was that on 27th April, 1880 George Garne took over Burford Brewery, the machinery and equipment, the Brewery House and three public houses: these were "The Royal Oak" at Burford with the two cottages adjoining, "The Plough" at Clanfield and "The Prince of Wales" at Shrivenham. This was on a ninety-nine year lease, paying £1,500 for the goodwill, a premium of £770, and a rent of £120 a year. T. H. Reynolds agreed to leave £2,000 in the business on which George paid seven and a half percent interest for five years. Reynolds also agreed to manage the business till Michaelmas 1880, when George,

THE BREWERY,

BURFORD, OXON.

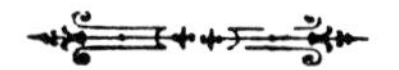

George Garne

Begs to announce that the annual dinner to his customers will take place at the Royal Oak, Witney Street, Burford, on "Fair Day," September 25th, between the hours of 11 a.m. and 3.30 p.m., when he will be pleased to give tickets to all his customers (man and wife, but not children) WHO DEAL EXCLUSIVELY WITH HIM AND HAVE NOT AN OVERDUE ACCOUNT.

Bills may be settled on "Fair Day."

Tickets to be obtained at the Brewery Office, Sheep Street, on "Fair Day," not later than 2.0. p.m.

THE BURFORD BRANCH

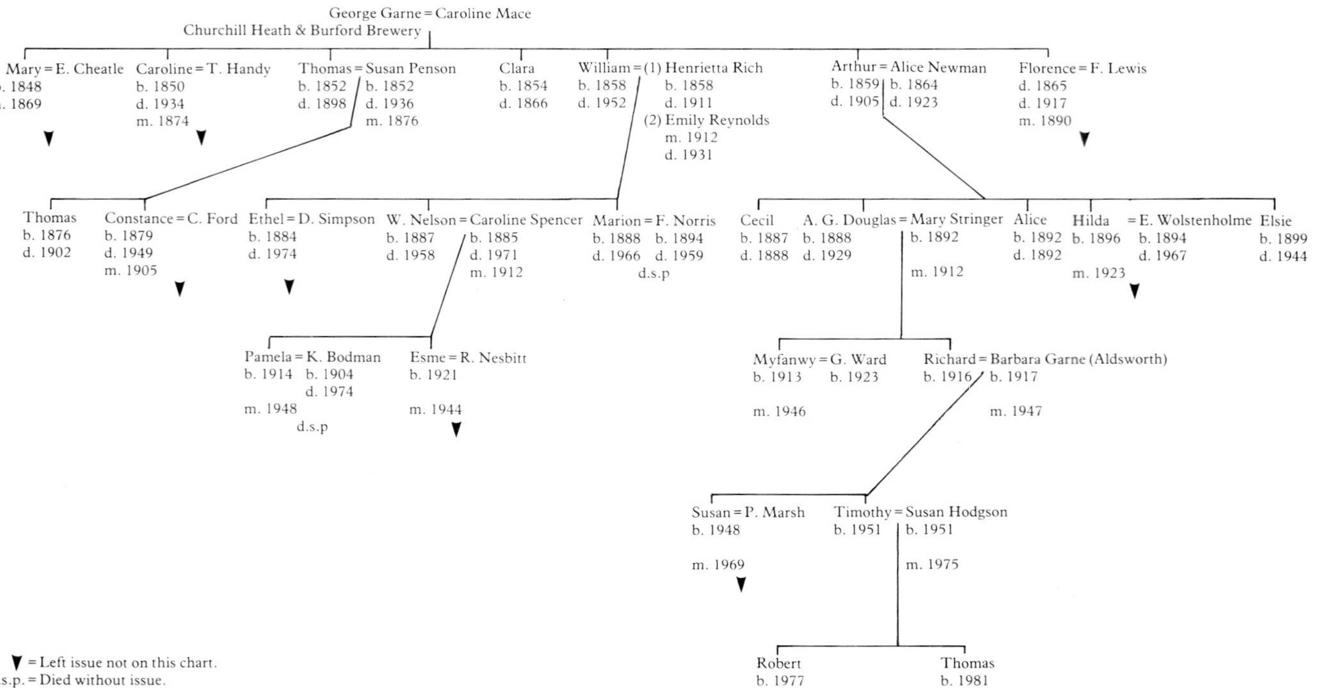

Caroline and their two sons, Willy and Arthur, a cook and a housemaid moved into The Brewery House.

George started trading in the early summer of 1880 as "George Garne, Brewer, Malster and Hop Merchant" selling beer to the three public houses and private houses all over the district delivered by brewer's dray, with an agent (known as an outride) to collect the orders by pony and trap. He also sold malt and hops to those who brewed their own beer.

At that time it was usual for all farmhouses and in fact private houses of all sorts to buy beer by the cask twice a year, keep it in the cellar and tap it as required. Garne's brewery sold family stock ale at one shilling a gallon, superior stock ale at one shilling and sixpence a gallon and mild beer at eight pence a gallon; in eighteen and thirty-six gallon casks.

By 1881 Willy was doing the brewing, Arthur was in the office doing the books and George was running the business employing nine men. It was not long before business expanded and over the next ten years the machinery and equipment was modernized and increased to a ten quarter plant (1 ton). The steam engine which drove all the machinery was built by Thomas Rose of Witney in 1855. It was run on coke and required a skilled man to operate it. It was still in use when brewing stopped in 1969.

The counting house was to one side of the main brewery entrance, a small room with a stone flagged floor, a small coal fire, a long desk with sloping top made of solid mahogany along which three people could work at large ledgers if they were standing up. Above this desk and looking at the main passage into the brewery was a long glass window, so that those working at the desk could see everything that went on in the main entrance which was wide enough to admit a horse and cart. On the shelf outside this window at one end was a small brass slot, so that those who came for a little yeast for breadmaking could put their penny in the slot, which fell into a locked drawer under the desk top inside. This part of the window could be opened so that orders could be taken without customers coming into the office.

This office remained unaltered for ninety years with three men standing up at the long desk. One of these was Willy Garne who occupied the position in the corner until he was ninety-one, still signing every cheque that left the business and still working a full day. Throughout this time smoking was not permitted in the office. Going into that office was like going into something out of Dickens.

Willy Garne. 1858-1952.

Arthur Garne. 1859-1905.

During 1882 a nephew of George Garne, Austin Hewer, one of his sisters seven sons came for a period to learn brewing from Willy Garne. He too was converted to being a Plymouth Brother. He became a brewer in the north of England. Austin Hewer's brother, Raymond, also became a brewer at Croydon.

Willy and Arthur

In the autumn of 1883 when he was twenty-five Willy married Henrietta Rich, known as Hetty. She was the daughter of a sea captain, master of one of the first steam ships "The Hanover". They took the tenancy of a tall Georgian house in Sheep Street, Burford and called it "Hanover".

Three years later Arthur married Alice Newman, known as Mellie, from her second name, Mahala. Alice was a daughter of John Newman who had come to Burford as an apprentice to a draper. He had come from Cirencester and married Jane Trinder, the chemist's daughter. By 1886 he had bought the business, rebuilt the shop in the High Street in the heavy Victorian style calling it Grafton House. Burford was still cut off from large towns so there was scope for a draper to branch out. John Newman had a horse and van which went round the whole district selling drapery, haberdashery, clothes, took orders for men's suits, hats and a wide variety of articles. He was also an undertaker.

Arthur and Mellie took a solid house at the top of the High Street called "East View" with a large garden which was an interest of Arthurs. He laid out a grass tennis court and bowling green and kept poultry and a calf and pony for his son.

In the next few years the number of public houses belonging to the brewery was increased by the purchase of The Jubilee Inn at Bampton for £650, The White Horse, High Street, Burford for £730, The Bull at Faringdon for £725 and The Queen's Arms at Faringdon for £1,470.

In 1895 George Garne took his two sons into partnership and the firm became known as Garne and Sons. A new lease with T. H. Reynolds was drawn up on very much the same terms as that of fifteen years earlier, but giving the Garnes the option to purchase for £3,000 closing on 29th September, 1927.

An annuity of £50 a year was to be paid to T. H. Reynolds and £20 a year to his wife. By now Reynolds was living at "Highview", a large house on the main turnpike road, later to be used as a hotel when the road became the A.40.

"Melly" Garne (née Newman). 1864-1923.

A. G. Douglas Garne. 1888-1929.

Business was still expanding so in 1895 trading in wines and spirits was begun. A wine and spirit store was built underneath the granaries so that large stocks could be held and the growing free trade supplied, much of it now by rail from Shipton Station, a village five miles to the north.

A bottling plant was installed and the sale of bottled beers and stout begun with a label which became well known in the district over the next seventy years.

Burford still had its annual hiring fair at Michaelmas when farmworkers came looking for fresh jobs and farmers came looking for men as was the custom to engage farm staff for a year. The streets were lined with booths and stalls and livestock was sold.

Nelson Garne. 1916.

George Garne kept the goodwill of the public and the name of the brewery well known, by inviting all those of his customers who had paid their bills, to a free cold lunch in the granary of the brewery. Large joints of ham and beef were sliced and blue pint china cups were filled with draught beer. Some years as many as six hundred people were entertained and the office was kept busy dealing with the overdue accounts.

This gathering became known as one of the social events of the year and was also a very good way of advertising Garne's Brewery.

Quite naturally George Garne's interest was still cattle-breeding and he was still in demand as a judge at major shows. He also spent some time advising his daughter and grandson, Caroline and Tom Handy on their farming at Hampen, Caroline's husband having died young.

In 1897 George and Caroline had their golden wedding and a big party was held in the granary with all the staff and their families invited. George was given a Bible by the staff and Caroline an umbrella. I'm not sure what if any was the significance of these gifts.

By now Willy and Hetty had two daughters and a son, Ethel and Marion (known as Topsy) and William Nelson Rich, known as Nelson to keep his mother's seafaring family tradition.

When she was old enough Willy would take Ethel in the gig on Sunday evenings to preach the Plymouth Brethren "word" round the villages. When he did this at Aldsworth parish his cousins strongly disapproved and thought this a very unbecoming practice for a member of the Garne family. In fact it was thought there might be an attempt to preach radical disaffection among the labourers, as sometimes the meetings were held in cottages.

The whole thing was summed up as "bloody psalm singers", no more beer was bought from Burford Brewery and the two families never spoke to each other again. Forty years later nothing had changed.

Arthur and Mellie meanwhile had five children, two boys and three girls; one boy and one girl died as babies leaving the son, Arthur George Douglas (known as Douglas) and two daughters, Hilda and Elsie very much younger.

Arthur had not the serious disposition of his brother but enjoyed games and going to horse-races. He became a J.P. He is always remembered as giving eggs from his poultry to any passing tramp who called, and there were plenty of vagrants at that time.

Tom, the auctioneer

No account of the Garne family in Burford at the end of the last century would be complete without mention of Thomas, George's eldest son and his family. Thomas was obviously the "black sheep" of the family, who had married Susan Penson at Churchill Heath and became an auctioneer and valuer. One of the problems for the geneologist is "black sheep". Few of the relatives will mention them, especially in a period such as late Victorian times when to be respectable, sober and industrious was the aim. Thomas was obviously none of these things. What he lived on after he ceased to belong to Acock, Hanks and Garne in 1882 is a mystery, although he still farmed Maughesbury Farm with a pedigree Shorthorn herd until 1887. There are documents in existence rubber stamped Thomas Garne, auctioneer and valuer, dated 1883 after he had left Acock and Hanks. It is known however that he moved to Burford to a house in Sheep Street next to "Hanover". Children never have the reticence or disapproval of "black sheep" of their parents, so Willy's eldest daughter, Ethel, when she was eighty-nine, remembered playing as a child with her cousins next door. Although Willy's children were forbidden to have anything to do with Thomas's children, a hole was made in the dividing hedge so that secret games could be played. Another hole led into the Newman's garden so that Arthur's children could join in.

Ethel also remembered the hushed conversations when her father or grandfather had to pay Thomas's debts, a frequent occurrence.

No more children were born to Thomas and Susan after they left Maughesbury Farm. There were only the two children, Thomas and Constance, born in the first three years of marriage. The reason for this is unknown. It is possible, you could even say probable, Thomas was an alcoholic.

The stories told by old people about him, forty years after his death, all relate to his liking for drink. There was the occasion when as an auctioneer he was required to sell the livestock for Robert Penson, his wife's uncle, at the latter's dispersal sale at Foxcote Farm, the next farm to Churchill Heath. Unfortunately Tom Garne drank too much at lunch and collapsed among the sheep he was selling, so that there was a delay until another auctioneer, James Tayler, could be found to carry on with the sale.

At that time there was scope for auctioneers of livestock. The repeal of the tax on auctions in the sixties had left the way open for good judges of livestock to start auction sales. John Thornton started in 1868 as an auctioneer and soon established a national reputation and a business still in existence today. He was able to sell cattle at twenty lots an hour. There is no evidence however of Tom Garne conducting auction sales after 1883.

When he died one January night in 1898 aged forty-six the doctor stated he died from an apoplectic fit. It is significant that he was buried at Fulbrook, the next village, and not at Burford. According to the newspaper account the funeral procession consisted of two carriages only. He left no will and no probate was granted so presumably he died penniless.

Tom, the Cricketer

The two children of Tom and Susan were a boy, Tom, and a girl, Constance. The boy was sent to Burford Grammar School as a day boy no doubt. By the time he was seventeen he was in the first XI at cricket and is mentioned in the school magazine of 1893 as the best bowler the school had ever had. Tom was tall and fair and a very fast bowler. At the time the sports master was G. L. Jessop who later became Captain of Gloucestershire and played for England.

When he left school Tom went to London to work for Maples, the furnishers in North London in their brass department. He is next heard of as playing club cricket for Clarence, which was Maples's sports club. This was in 1899 when he had a very successful season according to a book of newspaper cuttings he kept, now in the possession of his great nephew, Michael Ford. In a match against Cavendish, the sports club of Debenham and Freebody on 7th May, 1899 he took eighteen wickets for seventeen runs. He also broke a stump.

In 1900 he had another good season. When playing for "Bees" against London County he bowled W. G. Grace and also his brother. He twice played for Middlesex 2nd XI at Lords. There is an interesting letter from a club secretary to the Clarence secretary asking for a fixture, but on condition Garne did not play, as his bowling was so fast batsmen were afraid of injury.

Tom Garne played football for Clarence that winter and also took part in athletic sports.

Then comes a sudden change, for Tom joins the army. The Royal Artillery as a gunner; a most extraordinary thing to do in 1901, when the army was not enjoying a very good reputation and the life of a private soldier was rough to say the least of it. There was a certain amount of patriotic fervour brought about by the Boer War and there was a national appeal for volunteers for the army but few joined the ranks for patriotic motives. It was usually to avoid the police, debt or girls. Being a clerk in a London office cannot have seemed very adventurous and no doubt the salary was insufficient for one playing club cricket every weekend. With nothing inherited from his father it seems a possibilty that he joined the army to escape debts. Anyway in 1901 he was playing cricket for the Royal Artillery as Bombardier Garne. He was then posted to India where unfortunately he died in 1902 from sunstroke or pneumonia, I'm not sure which, and is buried in the military cemetary at Quetta.

It is a pity that army records of that period were all destroyed by German bombs on London in 1942.

Constance

When Tom the auctioneer died in 1898 his widow, Susan Penson, took a job as housekeeper to an old friend, a Mr. Bartlett of Hampton Grey, Kidlington near Oxford. He was a retired farmer who lived in a large house in style, with a big garden and a boat on the Thames. She is remembered by her grandchildren as dressing like Queen Victoria and being an autocratic old lady. She remained there for twenty years until Mr. Bartlett died, then she moved to be near her daughter.

Constance was nineteen when her father died. She had led a leisurely life, been well educated and was good looking. Nevertheless in 1898 the openings for a girl with no money were very limited indeed, but she took a job as a governess with a family called Hardy at Tisbury in Wiltshire.

After a time the Hardys moved to the Manor House at Swallowcliffe and Constance played the organ in the village church. Naturally she was in demand at social functions and was pursued by the young farmers of the district, one of whom, Charles Ford, she married in 1905.

The Fords had been tenant farmers on the Wardour estate at Hook Farm, Donhead St. Andrew for the previous hundred years.

Charles Ford was a good horseman and a dashing young sergeant in the Wiltshire Yeomanry, the local territorials. He won prizes galore at all the local point to points. He also liked a social life and plenty to drink. To the marriage there were three sons and a daughter.

The depression in farming in the twenties led to the farm being given up in 1928 and Charles taking jobs as farm manager.

Finally they moved to the Southampton area and took a house large enough to take in boarders. Here it was they both died.

* * *

Garne and Hewer

To return now to Burford at the turn of the century, where changes quickly came about. George died in 1902, an old man much respected in the district. The brewery was inherited jointly by his two sons, Willy and Arthur, and his widow, Caroline remained in the Brewery House for two more years until her death in 1904. Willy's religious scruples would not permit him to enter the church or churchyard for his parents' funerals.

When the Brewery House became empty on the death of Caroline, her youngest daughter, Florrie, moved in with her four children. She had married in 1890 Frank Lewis of Hereford, but what became of him is not known. Florrie remained in the Brewery House until Nelson and his wife took it over in 1913.

In 1904 there was a bad fire in the brewery which worried the partners whose children were mostly away at boarding schools. Willy's son was sent to a Plymouth Brethren school at Weston-Super-Mare, where in 1903 Nelson won the medal for the best scholar in the school. Arthur's son, Douglas, was sent first to Belmore House, a private school in Cheltenham and then to Eastbourne College, a new public school, which it was thought would be in a healthier area, where he was doing very well, until suddenly and without warning his father died.

It was in May 1905 that Arthur decided to go to the St. Leger at Newmarket. His wife, Mellie, often accompanied him on these trips but on this occasion the governess was ill and the two little girls could not be left alone so Arthur departed on his own. Later a telegram was received to say that Arthur had had a heart attack on the race-course, so Mellie set off in the brewery gig for Shipton Station to take the train to Newmarket. But she was too late. Arthur was dead before she arrived.

This of course caused upheaval in the brewery. Douglas was fetched back from school to help with the brewing and Willy was faced with the problem of paying Arthur's widow her half share of the business without selling any stock or property. The brewery, machinery and

Burford Brewery, 1879

stock was valued at £8,426 9s 9d of which £5,373 5s 3d was still owed to Thomas Reynolds and £3,048 6s 6d to Arthur's executors.

In the event Willy overcame most of his problems by inviting his cousin Austin Hewer to come into partnership with him. This had the advantage that Hewer would put £1,500 into the business. He was a strong member of the Plymouth Brethren sect, an experienced brewer and a man of Willy's own age. This meant a few years later Douglas was pushed out of the business, so Mellie and her three children moved to London to stay with Mary Cheatle. She was Arthur's eldest sister who had married Dr. Cheatle and moved to London. By this time Mary was a widow and her four children had left home.

Later Mellie and her children rented a house in Frenchay Road, Oxford. After a few years she moved to Portland Road, Oxford where she died in 1923.

Austin Hewer moved into a house called "The Lodge", High Street, Burford in 1905 and a new partnership deed was drawn up on much the same lines as that between Willy and Arthur. The business continued to trade as Garne and Sons. There was one marked difference, however. Hewer's religious scruples would not permit him to sell beer in public houses although he did not mind making it. So the partnership let the three original pubs to W. G. Garne for £40 a year and he would receive 12½% on the sale of the beer. The pubs which had been bought subsequent to the original deal with Reynolds had been owned jointly by Willy and Arthur.

The new lease allowed each partner to draw £35 per month from the business and to bring in one son each to the partnership sharing the capital of his father.

Willy's son, Nelson had started engineering training in London, where he lodged in the house of a Miss Harrod whose family owned a department store, but on Douglas's departure Nelson was recalled to Burford to work in the brewery and learn the business.

Nelson's eldest sister, Ethel, married Dudley Simpson who had a iron and steel business in the Midlands. They had two daughters.

Then in 1911 Hetty, Willy's wife, died. Willy was very lonely and in the following year married Emily Reynolds, a niece of T. H. Reynolds who had previously owned the brewery. They spent their honeymoon at the Regent Palace Hotel in London, which seems a bit out of character, but Emily was not a member of the Plymouth Brethren sect. The marriage was not a happy one. No one ever visited "Hanover",

Emily disliked all the Garne family and slept in the attic. She could be heard shouting at Willy and sometimes threw saucepans at him. He spent most of his time at the brewery.

The same year as his father's second marriage Nelson married Caroline Spencer from Harrogate who he had first met when she was at school at Malvern with his sister.

On the outbreak of the Great War Nelson joined the 2nd/1st Huntingdon Cyclist Battalion, who were stationed at Cromer in Norfolk. His wife and baby daughter joined him there, where they remained throughout the war. He with the rank of captain. When the war ended they moved back into the Brewery House which had fallen vacant on the death of Florrie Lewis, Nelson's Aunt. They changed the name of the house to "Barraca" (Spanish for "The Hut").

Under the terms of the lease of 1895 with T. H. Reynolds, there was an option to buy for £3,000. With inflation due to the war, by 1918 this figure was very cheap, so the brewery, the machinery, the three original pubs and Barraca were all bought for £3,000 in three instalments of £1,000 in February, May and July 1918.

In the same period three more pubs were bought, The Lamb, next door to the brewery, The Plough at Alvescot and The Griffen at Witney. The latter was acquired through the inability of the landlord to pay for his supplies over a long period.

In May of 1922 Nelson was taken into the partnership with a half share of his father. The national depression which followed resulted in a falling off of trade so that in 1929 The Lamb was sold to finance the building of a new bottling plant. Brewing was down to thirty barrels a week.

Garne and Sons Ltd.

In May 1930 the business was turned into a private company trading as Garne and Sons Ltd. The directors were W. G. Garne, A. E. Hewer, W. R. N. Garne and E. Jeffs. Ernest Jeffs had first started work in 1893 as a boy in the brewery and by 1930 he was the buyer.

Garne's Brewery had always had a good reputation as an employer. Most of the staff of twenty stayed for years and many worked their whole life for the brewery.

In 1931 Emily Garne (Mrs. W.G.) died. She had left instructions that she was to be buried in London and none of her possessions were to be touched by any of the Garne family. Willy was seventy-three and thereafter spent more time with his son and daughter-in-law at "Barraca", where there were two granddaughters, Pamela aged seventeen and Esme aged ten, whose social life was limited by the restrictions of the Plymouth Brethren. But Willy's principals permitted him to take home a bottle of port from the brewery on frequent occasions and he was known to entertain his family with champagne.

Business must have been looking up by 1932 as a new pub, The Beehive, was built at Carterton and opened in September of that year. It was no longer economic to produce malt on such a small scale so malting was discontinued. After the war in 1946 the malthouse was converted into a flat for Willy who was still living alone. He had his dinner every day in the Lamb next door. Hours of business as published in the 1938 price list remained the same, i.e. 7.00 a.m. Monday to Friday and 7.00 a.m. till 1.00 p.m. on Saturday.

In 1951 Willy was finally unable to carry on working in the office and signing every cheque that went out. Since he was ninety-two and had spent seventy-five years working in the brewery this was not surprising. He was forced to hand over his clerical duties to Frank Wilkinson, who had come into the counting house straight from Burford Grammar School in 1930 to help the clerk, Burton. These three had stood at the long mahogany desk every weekday for the last twenty years, apart from the war years, which Frank Wilkinson had spent in the Tank Corps, and although seriously wounded had returned to his desk.

In this twenty years nothing had changed; Austin Hewer, now aged eighty-six still sat in the private office upstairs on the other side of a large mahogany table to Nelson Garne, aged only sixty-three. Ernest Jeffs was still the buyer aged seventy-one.

All letters were still written in pencil with carbon copies on specially printed pads. A small typewriter had been bought in the 1930's but no typist was employed. It was not until Frank Wilkinson returned from the war that anyone could use it, he having taught himself to type while convalescent in the army.

Changes now came about quickly; Frank Wilkinson was made a director in March 1952, since he was doing the bulk of the management. Then in November 1952 Nelson's eldest daughter, Pamela's husband, Keith Bodman was made a director. He was an executive of Barclays Bank. Alan Hewer, Austin's son, became a director in 1955.

In the meanwhile Nelson bought a large house at Milford-on-Sea in

Hampshire. His sister, Ethel and her husband had bought a house here in 1938 and the whole family had always gone there for holidays. So Willy was moved to Milford and Nelson retired there. Nelson's daughter, Topsy and her husband, Lt. Col. Leslie Norris also retired there.

In 1953 Willy Garne, Austin Hewer and Ernest Jeffs all died the same year each having spent their entire life in the service of Burford Brewery.

When Nelson died in 1958, Frank Wilkinson who had become managing director in 1953 ran the business for the next eleven years single handed with Keith Bodman calling in from time to time.

Finally in April 1969 Wadworths of Devizes acquired the share capital of Garne and Sons Ltd., which was owned by Mrs. Nelson Garne, A. V. Hewer, K. Bodman, Mrs. Bodman, Esme Nesbitt and F. R. Wilkinson. Brewing continued for six months more until in September 1969 it finally stopped, thus ending one hundred and seventy years of brewing in Burford by one of the smallest breweries in the country; ninety years being in Garne hands.

The brewery was thereafter used as a bottle store and the nine tied houses changed their signs from Garnes to Wadworths. Port and sherry though was still sold with the Garne label.

The great-grandson of George Garne, the founder of the brewery is Douglas's only son, Richard, the writer of this history, who having married Will Garne of Aldsworth's fourth daughter, Barbara, and managed a large Cotswold farm is in a position to set down this record.

A group of "foreign" buyers. Leaning on the fence (left to right) F. G. Minchin, Cobberley, Cheltenham, looking for 30 to 40 calves to sell as forward stores, A. T. Garne, Cheltenham; W. McDowall and Charles Goodger, Chichester; Oscar Colburn behind in cap.

CHAPTER X

The Dursley Branch

Bibury

One of the Sherborne Yeomen, John Garne born in 1660 married Anne and they had seven children, three sons and four daughters. The youngest son, Thomas, remained in Sherborne but his brother, Richard, moved to Bibury, a parish on the Coln River about eight miles south of Sherborne. There he married a Bibury girl, Ann Haines in 1736. There is no record of any children in Bibury, but this could be due to the very poor church registers. It is clear, however, that another Sherborne Garne family, Richard's first cousin, William and his wife, Elizabeth, also moved to Bibury twenty years later as their two youngest sons, Richard and Thomas, were both born in Bibury, both were married there. Richard married Mary Maisey from a well known local landowning family and one of Richard's daughters, Hannah, was married there in 1813. So it would seem Garnes were in Bibury for about a hundred years. Presumably they too were yeoman, although the parish records are so brief they do not mention it.

For many years Bibury had been noted for the woollen cloth industry carried out by independent weavers in their own homes. There was also a fulling mill on the River Coln and the cloth was dried on tenter racks beside the river on a piece of ground known to this day as Rack Island.

It is possible this branch of the family were also engaged in the woollen trade, as many yeoman families at that time combined farming and weaving.

They certainly had tombstones in Bibury churchyard the inscriptions on which unfortunately are now no longer legible, two of Richard's sons, John and William, moved to Uley, near Dursley. The reason for this can only be guessed. Possibly there was no room on the family farm, enclosures were making it difficult for young men to remain in farming. There was also a slump in the woollen trade. The eldest brother, John, married and had four daughters in the first quarter of the

THE BIBURY & ULEY BRANCH

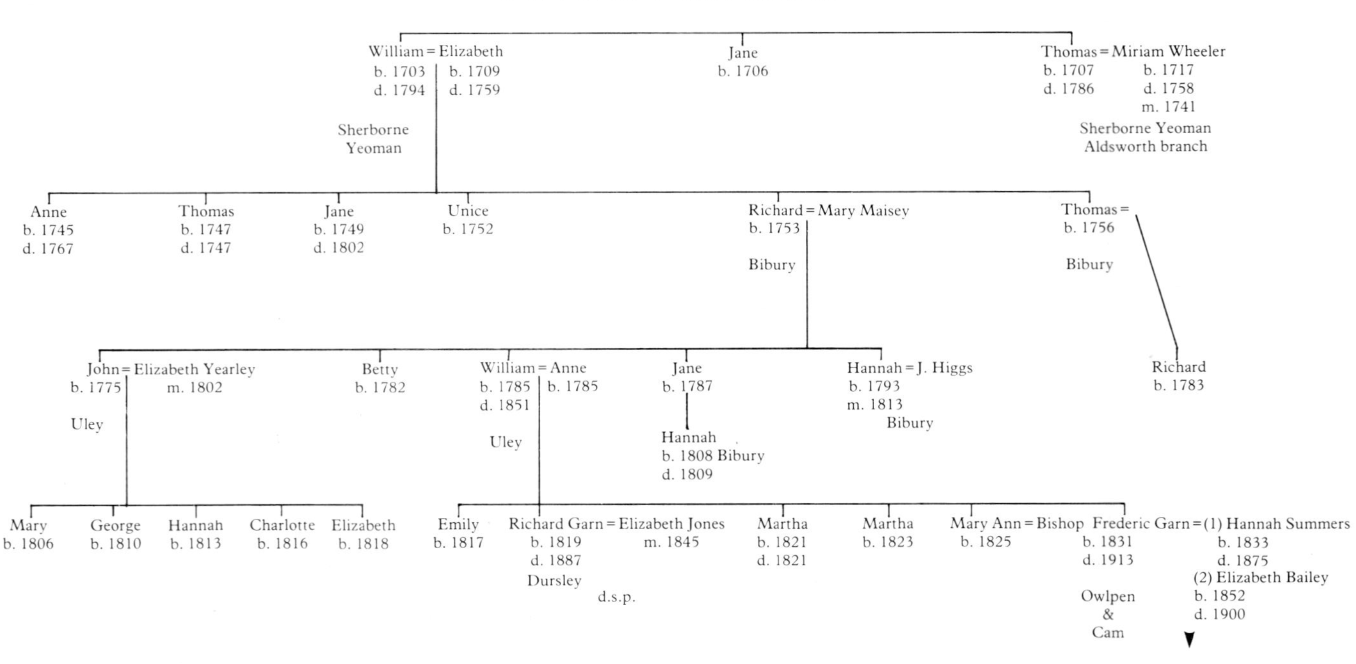

The name spelled Garn after 1820

Upthorpe
Lower Cam
Green Street
Far Green
Ham Fm
Nympsfield
Woodfield
Mills
Cam
Ashmead Ho
Ashmead Green
Cam Long Down
Tilsdown
Peaked Down
Hodgecombe Fm
West Hill
Crawley
Uley Bury
Woodrock
Kingshill
Engineering Works
Hydegate
Downham Hill
Uley
Owlpen
Dursley
Woodmancote
Rockstowes
Sheephouse Fm
Shadwell
Elcombe
Bencombe
Whiteway
Millend
Forthay
Pitt Court
The Ridge
Symonds' Hall Fm
Ashel Barn
North Nibley
Waterley Bottom
Nibley Knoll
Westridge Wood
The Ridings
Barnhill Fm
Brackenbury Ditches
Howley
Bournstream
Sawcombe Fm
Bagpath
Coombe Hill
Coombe
Tyley Bottom
Scrubbett's Fm
Holywell
Bradley
Ozleworth
Ozleworth Park
Merlin Haven
Newark Park
Yewtree Hill
Wotton-under-Edge
Boxwell
Sewage Wks
Textile Mill
Hawpark Fm
Little Tor Hill
Wortley Hill
Kingswood
Wortley
Nind Fm
Cross Roads Lodge
Stonehill Wood
Upper Barns Fm
Park Fm
Alderley Wood
Burdon Court Fm
Rose Hill (Sch)
Alderley
Tresham
Glentworth Fm
Folly Fm
Haroldsfield Fm
Lower Wltheymoore
Hillesley
B 4058
B 4060
B 4066
A 4135

nineteenth century. His brother, William, married, in the early years of the century, Anne of Upton on Severn in Worcestershire and they had six children. In the parish registers both the brothers names are spelled Garn which spelling has continued for many members of this branch of the family to this day.

Owlpen

William became the tenant of Summerfield Farm, Owlpen, a small hilly village about three miles from Dursley, sometime after 1831, the year his youngest child, Frederic, was born. In the baptism register for Frederic, William is described as a mason and the name spelled Garne.

William and Anne's eldest son, Richard married Elizabeth Jones from a local family but had no children. Richard had his own glaziers business at Cam, near Dursley.

On William's death in 1851 his youngest son, Frederic, carried on the tenancy of Summerfield Farm (fifty acres) with his mother. He was twenty at the time.

According to William's will made the day before he died in September 1851 the farm was leasehold. He left the farm, live and dead stock and all his possessions to his three children, Richard, Mary Ann Bishop and Frederic.

Frederic married Hannah Summers a farmer's daughter in 1863. They had eight children and Hannah died at the age of forty-two with the birth of the youngest. Frederic married again three years later Elizabeth Bailey also from a local farming family said to be of Welsh extraction. She must have been a remarkable woman. She married Frederic, a man twenty-one years older than herself with seven children under fourteen and he with the tenancy of a fifty acre farm at the beginning of a serious agricultural depression in the wettest year for a century. They then had seven more children in thirteen years, so that on her death at the age of forty-eight Frederic had fifteen children. It is not surprising that a contemporary letter says Frederic had a hot temper.

In spite of his difficulties Frederic managed to find time for considerable public service. He was a member of the Dursley Board of Guardians, which administered the poor law, for forty-seven years. He was churchwarden at Owlpen for thirty-two years and at Cam for fourteen years, a remarkable record.

To this day he is remembered in the area by Garn Close at Uley. In

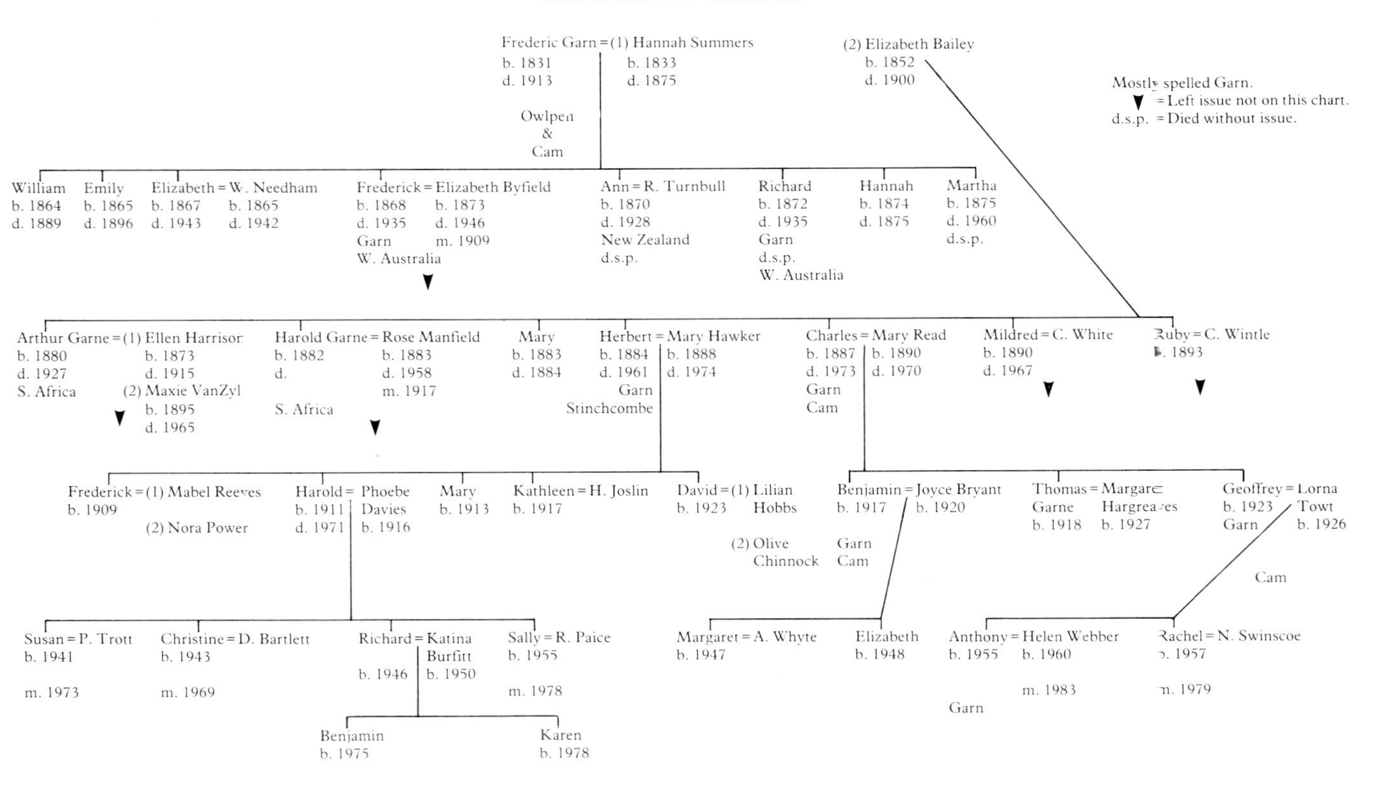
THE DURSLEY BRANCH
Frederic Garn = (1) Hannah Summers
b. 1831 d. 1913
b. 1833 d. 1875
Owlpen & Cam
(2) Elizabeth Bailey
b. 1852 d. 1900
Mostly spelled Garn.
= Left issue not on this chart.
d.s.p. = Died without issue.
William b. 1864 d. 1889
Emily b. 1865 d. 1896
Elizabeth = W. Needham
b. 1867 d. 1943
b. 1865 d. 1942
Frederick = Elizabeth Byfield
b. 1868 d. 1935 Garn W. Australia
b. 1873 d. 1946 m. 1909
Ann = R. Turnbull
b. 1870 d. 1928 New Zealand d.s.p.
Richard b. 1872 d. 1935 Garn d.s.p. W. Australia
Hannah b. 1874 d. 1875
Martha b. 1875 d. 1960 d.s.p.
Arthur Garne = (1) Ellen Harrison
b. 1880 d. 1927 S. Africa
b. 1873 d. 1915
(2) Maxie VanZyl b. 1895 d. 1965
Harold Garne = Rose Manfield
b. 1882 d. S. Africa
b. 1883 d. 1958 m. 1917
Mary b. 1883 d. 1884
Herbert = Mary Hawker
b. 1884 d. 1961 Garn Stinchcombe
b. 1888 d. 1974
Charles = Mary Read
b. 1887 d. 1973 Garn Cam
b. 1890 d. 1970
Mildred = C. White
b. 1890 d. 1967
Ruby = C. Wintle
b. 1893
Frederick = (1) Mabel Reeves
b. 1909
(2) Nora Power
Harold = Phoebe Davies
b. 1911 d. 1971
b. 1916
Mary b. 1913
Kathleen = H. Joslin
b. 1917
David = (1) Lilian Hobbs
b. 1923
(2) Olive Chinnock
Benjamin = Joyce Bryant
b. 1917 Garn Cam
b. 1920
Thomas = Margaret Hargreaves
Garne b. 1918
b. 1927
Geoffrey = Lorna Towt
b. 1923 Garn
b. 1926
Cam
Susan = P. Trott
b. 1941 m. 1973
Christine = D. Bartlett
b. 1943 m. 1969
Richard = Katina Burfitt
b. 1946
b. 1950
Sally = R. Paice
b. 1955 m. 1978
Margaret = A. Whyte
b. 1947
Elizabeth b. 1948
Anthony = Helen Webber
b. 1955 Garn
b. 1960 m. 1983
Rachel = N. Swinscoe
b. 1957 m. 1979
Benjamin b. 1975
Karen b. 1978

1892 Frederic and his family moved to Street Farm, Cam, a sixty acre farm belonging to the Berkley estate. The following year he founded a pedigree dairy Shorthorn herd.

Just how many the family consisted of at this time is not clear. The eldest son, William, had died aged twenty-five. There were two sons, Fred, (twenty-four) and Dick (twenty) who probably helped on the farm. There were four daughters who may have left home although possibly the eldest, Emily, (twenty-seven) who never married, stayed to help her mother with the five children under fourteen and the baby due to be born the following year. Two baby girls had died previously. This was a period of agricultural depression in which large numbers of men were leaving the land. Those with enterprise and a little money emigrated to the colonies in large numbers looking for a better life. It is not surprising therefore that Frederic, Richard and Ann, later followed by Arthur and Harold, all emigrated. Emily died in 1896 and her stepmother, Elizabeth, in 1900. This left Martha, the only single daughter, at home looking after the four youngest children.

Cam

As has so often been the case it was the youngest son who remained at home and worked the farm with his father. Herbert moved to Bristol to run a Dairy business, where he married and had five children. But when the Great War was over he returned to the Dursley area and took the tenancy of Stancombe Park Farm, about two hundred acres. In 1928 the lease expired and he was forced to move to a farm at Ampney St. Mary near Cirencester. The cattle were moved in the traditional way on foot with the children as drovers. Times were very bad, the farming depression was general and in 1930 Herbert was forced to give up farming and take his family to Bristol to take up the Dairy business again. The children of Herbert and Mary were three sons, Fred and Harold who worked for the Post Office and David who joined the navy and retired as a Chief Petty Officer, and two daughters, Mary and Kathleen. The whole family were still in this area forty years later.

Shortly after his father's death Charles married a neighbouring farmer's daughter, Mary Read and they took a farm in Somerset. However when Mary's father died they returned to Cam and carried on the tenancy of his farm, Church Farm. They had three sons, the eldest of whom, Ben, became a partner with his father on the farm and two younger sons, Tom and Geoffrey, followed other occupations.

The Emigrants

The first to sail to the other side of the world was Ann who went to New Zealand. There she married a Mr. R. Turnbull but had no children. She remained there for the rest of her life near Auckland and died aged fifty-eight.

She was followed by her elder brother, Frederic, who went to join her. He then went on to Western Australia and took part in the "gold rush" to Kalgoorlie. Whether he found any gold was never recorded but he did remain in that area for the rest of his life, one of the pioneers who endured tremendous hardships and who largely by patient hard manual work opened up that area of Western Australia, north-east of Perth. At that time the land was partly wooded, fairly flat, fertile and scrub covered but very dry. Kangeroos ranged everywhere. The whole area was largely uninhabited.

Frederic settled at a place called Benjaberring about one hundred and twenty miles north-east of Perth. With a few men working for him he was given a government contract to supply timber sleepers for the new railway being pushed out from Perth to Kalgoorlie. All the work was by hand with axe and cross cut saw. Living was in timber shacks in Sawyer's Valley.

Near the new railway a settlement grew up called Wyalkatchem (an Aboriginal word). This was declared a parish in 1908 and was a centre for all the necessities of life, shops, bank, doctor, church and so forth.

The land was being sold by the government in blocks to settlers prepared to fence, clear and cultivate. Frederick bought about fifteen hundred acres at a low price freehold on condition he erected a three wire fence all round. It was surveyed in straight lines with wooden posts driven in to mark the boundary. He then built a three room timber house roofed with corrugated iron, an open fire and oven and a three thousand gallon rainwater tank.

It was not until 1909 when he was forty-one that Frederick married Elizabeth Byfield of Australian parents. She was thirty-six. They had three children, the eldest of whom, Anne, died at the age of three. They were able to move into the new house in 1915. Slowly the land was cleared, horses and implements were bought and wheat was planted.

Frederick's younger brother, Richard (Dick), had gone to the Boer War in 1900 and stayed on afterwards in South Africa. In 1910 he went to Western Australia and worked for his brother, Frederick, for some years before starting farming on his own, but he never married.

THE EMIGRANTS

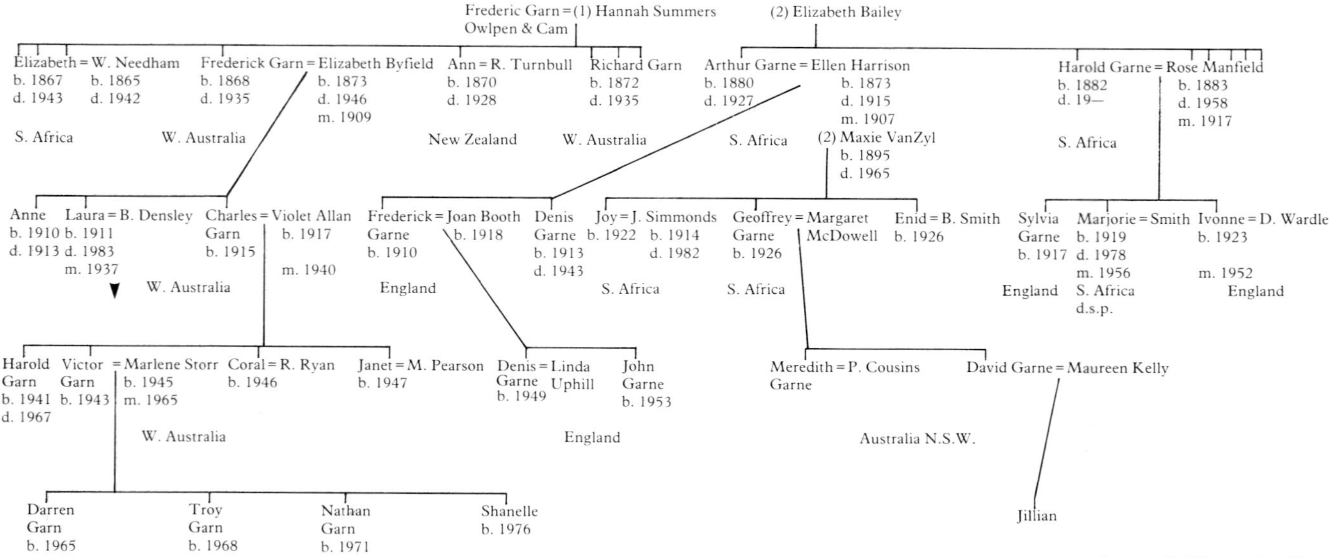

Some spelled Garne, others Garn.

Church Farm, Cam, 1924. Charles, Mary, Ben, Thomas and Geoffrey Garn.

Stancombe Park Farm, Stinchcombe. Herbert Garn and his sons Frederick and Harold.

When Frederick and Elizabeth's two children were seven years old they were old enough to ride a pony to school five miles away. This was a one room bungalow where one woman teacher taught ten children. Horses were the ony motive power on the farm until a model T. Ford was bought in the 1920's.

The keeping of sheep was started when an eight foot fence had been erected round a paddock to keep out the Dingo dogs. The children then had to bring the sheep into a yard every night.

Wyalkatchem became the centre of a large wheat belt and was the first place in Australia in 1931 to instal the bulk handling of wheat at the railway run by a farmer's co-operative.

The worldwide depression of the 20's and 30's hit Australia very badly. Frederick's only son, Charles, who had been sent to boarding school in Perth had to be brought back to the farm in 1930. Richard was forced to give up farming and work for other farmers as a farming contractor.

Street Farm, Cam. Prize winning dairy Shorthorns. Charles Garn on right.

Frederick died in 1935 aged sixty-seven, leaving his son, Charles, aged twenty to carry on. His daughter, Laura, married a local farmer, Ben Densley in 1937. Richard died in 1935.

In 1940 Charles married Violet (Dot) Allan and they had four children. The farm had been increased to three thousand four hundred acres by this time. Over the next forty years this was to increase to ten thousand acres with a flock of five thousand sheep.

Emigration to the colonies continued throughout the early years of the twentieth century. Those who had left England first wrote back about their new life and opportunities in new countries. In England the agricultural depression had only slightly improved, so large numbers of farmer's sons and farm workers emigrated.

Street Farm, Cam, 1913. Charles (26); Frederic (82); Martha (38) Garn.

By 1893 Frederic Garn's second wife, Elizabeth, had had seven children and there were still living at home two daughters of the first marriage so it was not surprising that as soon as they were old enough the two eldest boys, Arthur and then Harold, sailed for South Africa and settled in Cape Town after the Boer War was over.

Arthur Garne married in 1907 an English girl, Ellen Harrison, who had also emigrated and was running a millinery business. They had two sons. Unfortunately Ellen died in 1915, so Arthur made his way back to England so that his two boys could be brought up by his wife's sister in Bedford. He then returned to South Africa and married again, Maxie Van Zyl, a girl of Dutch extraction. A daughter was born in 1922 and then twins, a boy and a girl in 1926.

Harold Garne did not marry until 1917, Rose Manfield, and they had three daughters. Unfortunately the family had a very hard time due to Harold's drink problem. The only person who could help him was his brother, Arthur, so on Arthur's death in 1927, Rose left her husband and brought her three children to England and settled in Devonshire. It has proved to be impossible to trace when or where Harold died.

Arthur Garne 1880-1927. Denis and Frederick.

Denis Garne, 1913-43. Died as P.O.W. on Burma railway.

CHAPTER XI

The Great War and After

Cocklebarrow

In Chapter VII I outlined the tragic death by drowning in the River Wye of George Garne of Baysham Court when he was only thirty-three, leaving a widow, Marian Tayler and two babies.

She moved back to her family area at Northleach as housekeeper to her single brother, who was manager of the Tayler brewery. When the problem of her son, Arthur's, education came up she moved to Cheltenham and sent him to a private school, Belmore House, where he met his cousin, Douglas Garne, of the Burford brewery.

The influence of Harry Garne, the housemaster of Wellingborough, who was Marian's brother-in-law, was such that many Garne boys for the next fifty years would be sent there. Arthur recalled that in his first term going to Wellingborough in the same carriage was his cousin, Tom, from Aldsworth, who smoked a pipe the whole time.

On leaving school at the age of seventeen, Arthur was sent to work at a bank in Oxford, his mother and sister having taken a house there. He disliked the bank however and particularly disliked working indoors, so was very glad when the opportunity came to be taken onto the farm of his Uncle Tayler at Cold Aston.

Then came the chance he wanted in 1911 when he was twenty-one, to be taken into the house of his wealthy kinsman, W.T. Garne, as farm assistant. W. T. was somewhat of an autocratic Victorian who spoke very little, but overawed most of those with whom he came in contact, many of whom were frightened of him. At least Arthur had a supporter and confidant in W.T.'s wife, the second Mrs. Garne.

Unlike many farmhouses of the period this one had all the signs of prosperity and expensive living—plenty of the best of everything. Entertainment of visitors and foreign buyers of pedigree livestock went on most of the year.

All this came to an end with the outbreak of the Great War, which was to change the way of life of all those remote farming villages of the Cotswolds. The surplus of farm workers turned into a shortage as men of all walks of life volunteered for the army. Arthur joined the Gloucestershire Yeomanry, a territorial horsed cavalry regiment with large numbers of farmer's sons but he was invalided out and returned to the farm, where he found himself in charge of the labour force of a few pensioners and twenty-five women. He found it necessary to take part in manual work himself, a practice which was unheard of for a farmer or his family on large Cotswold farms before the war.

Arthur was still determined to start farming on his own account even with the very little capital left him by his father. The opportunity came in 1918 when Cocklebarrow Farm at Aldsworth fell vacant and the Sherborne estate agreed to let it to him for £1 an acre, an average rent for the area in 1918. It was a large arable farm with a large stone farmhouse, so Arthur's mother moved in as housekeeper and all went well until the unexpected slump in farm prices of 1922. Prices of most farm products, grain, wool, lamb and beef halved in one year, so for anyone without capital to fall back on, the prospect was very bleak. Many newcomers to farming lost everything, including many ex-servicemen.

Landlords naturally were also badly affected. Lord Sherborne dropped the rent of Cocklebarrow to 10/- an acre and many farms were let at much less. Once more it was difficult to find tenants with enough capital and ability to take on large Cotswold farms. Thousands of acres reverted to weeds and rough grass as arable farming became uneconomic. Farm wages fell from £2 a week after the war to 28/6, and even at that low level farmers everywhere reduced staff. Farm workers moved to the towns whenever there was a chance of a better job and somewhere to live. Many farmers of large acreages adopted the system known as "dog and stick" which meant employing as few men as possible and running store cattle over most of the farm on rough grazing. There were many poor Cotswold hill farms being let for as little as half-a-crown an acre.

Naturally buildings, walls and cottages fell into disrepair as the depression set in for the next fifteen years.

In order to keep going Arthur Garne at Cocklebarrow started milking cows and running a retail milk round with a van which he drove personally. His mother kept house for him, his sister having married John Holder, a farmer from the North Cotswolds.

Mr. W. Garne

In 1927 he married Helen (Nelsie) Minchin, younger sister of his cousin, Will Garne's wife, after an engagement of seven years. They had one daughter, Joan.

Garne of Aldsworth

In Aldsworth at the same time there were two other Garne families, W.T. and his wife in Taylers House and his second son, Tom at Ladbarrow with his wife and three boys. W.T.'s eldest son, Will, living at Ablington with his wife, son and six daughters.

Towards the end of the Great War W.T. took Will into partnership running the three farms, Green Farm, Ablington and Swyre Farm. By now W.T. was an old man and had difficulty getting about due to hip trouble. He drove round the farm in a low four wheeler. Whenever he came to a gate he would blow a hunting horn and the nearest farmworker would come and open it for him.

In 1925 he died and Will and his family moved into Taylers House with his stepmother who lived in the best rooms waited on by her step grandchildren, a housekeeper and a maid or two.

It had always been expected that a fortune would be inherited on W.T.'s death, so there was general disappointment when the will was read. Although Will was in partnership with his father he was not in his confidence. Like so many farmers of the period W.T. never told anyone of his business affairs, and since there was very little book-keeping done it was not realised that the farms had been running at a loss for years. The Naunton Farm had been sold as well as Hinton House in Ablington. In the event Will and his brother, Tom, inherited two fifths each and their sister, Bessie, one fifth. Bessie was so put out by this disappointment that a quarrel with her two brothers continued for the rest of her life, about forty years, although the terms of the will could hardly be said to be their fault.

Much of Will's portion was wrapped up in the land, cottages, Tayler's House, buildings, Cotswold sheep and the Shorthorn herd and the amount of cash was small.

Will was forty-five when his father died and although not his father's favourite, Will had had his own way all his life and continued to do so. He had been brought up to have everything he wanted, but with a strict Victorian discipline and high standard of conduct. His word was his bond and seldom was anything written down, except cattle pedigrees and then preferably by someone else. Foxhunting was his chief interest in winter-time. He had started hunting with the V.W.H. (Earl Bathurst's) hunt at the age of ten and continued to do so until he was

Cotswold sheep at Aldsworth, Gloucestershire, 50 years ago. With them is their shepherd, Jim Wilcox.

well over eighty. He never missed a meet if he could possibly help it and as he lived his whole life in Ablington and Aldsworth parishes with seldom a night away, his knowledge of that Cotswold country was unsurpassed.

His second main interest was his herd of pedigree Shorthorn cattle with which he had spent his whole life. He was an acknowledged expert and judge of this breed and other beef breeds. He frequently judged at major British shows but never abroad.

His third love was his flock of Cotswold sheep which had been in his family for so long and which he was determined to keep even though everyone else gave them up. So for thirty years his was the only flock of Cotswolds remaining in Britain gradually getting more inbred. Fortunately he lived to see a revival of interest in old breeds of sheep and the Cotswold flock book was restarted in 1966 with Will as President at the age of eighty-six.

Another of Will's interests which at that time was very lucrative, was the breeding of modern Black Red game fowls. He would show the cockerels at shows up and down the country and sell them for high prices. The breeding and rearing of these birds took a lot of time and care, with which his large family of children were not allowed to help. The Victorian tradition of not allowing the women or children of the family to have anything to do with the farming persisted. Black breasted game fowls had been a lucrative sideline with Will's father and his great Uncle Robert.

Cotswold villages were often a long way apart and the only form of transport was the horse as it had been for hundreds of years. This meant opportunities for meeting for young people were rare. There were tennis parties and picnics in the summer, hunting, shooting parties and dances in winter.

Roads were dusty tracks in summer and muddy rutted in winter. No tarmacadam was used and roads were repaired by breaking up stones and filling the potholes. Nevertheless this did not deter the young. It was quite common for a young farmer to ride his horse across country to a dance in evening dress with his tail coat tucked up. Engagements and marriages were great social occasions.

Life was necessarily very narrow, with no telephone, radio or daily newspapers. News of the outside world only came by the weekly carriers cart and a weekly paper or two to each village. The affairs of the locality were more important to most people than national matters.

Certainly the local paper "The Wiltshire and Gloucestershire Standard" contained national news, stock exchange prices and foreign affairs all mixed up with local news.

When in 1922 the great slump came and land values halved in one year the type of farming being carried on at Aldsworth was hit badly, but Will's ideas were strictly conservative and he resisted change in everything. He did have a motor car for convenience but disliked it and only drove it for necessity and made no attempt to understand it.

Will would not change his methods to meet changing conditions and got by through being an owner occupier and allowing property to deteriorate.

Fortunately there was still a demand for good Shorthorn beef bulls, at the production of which he was an expert. He was ably assisted in this by the herdsman, Albert Forsyth who kept the cattle in tip top condition and produced prize winning bulls for the show ring.

Cotswold ram lambs were still sold by auction in Norfolk and used as crossing rams but the prices had dropped badly and the demand declined every year.

The fact that there was still a serious farming depression going on during the 20's and 30's was not so obvious on the Green Farm as on many other farms. The same policy was followed and the same staff kept with wages at 30/- a week. Hunting, shooting and tennis parties continued. As is so often the case it was the wife behind the scenes who really kept everything going. Her thrift and good management maintained the high standards. When all indoor staff had gone she and her six daughters when they were not at school ran this large house, poultry, gardening, grass tennis court, entertaining and parties.

The only son, Billy, was sent to Shaftesbury Grammar School where his Uncle Charles Tovey was headmaster and another Uncle Bob Minchin was a master. Billy was encouraged to take part in hunting and shooting but he was also required to work on the farm.

The Victorian system of money still operated, that was that Will alone handled the money, no member of the family received wages, all housekeeping requirements were bought on credit and paid for monthly by cheque. Will's wife, Frances, was expected to get by with the sale of any by-products and a little petty cash. Billy would get by with the sale of rabbits he would catch on the farm. This of course was not good training for the management of a complex business but it did teach the value of money.

Throughout this time it had never been necessary to name either the house or the farm where Will and his family lived. Like his father before him he was so well known a detailed address was unnecessary, he was merely Garne of Aldsworth.

Ladbarrow again

Will's brother, Tom, had taken the tenancy of Ladbarrow Farm on the Sherborne estate in Aldsworth in 1912 with his wife, Helen Wakefield (known as Nell) and one son. Two more boys were born during the Great War and all three were sent to school at Wellingborough. The eldest, Robert, joined his father on the farm, the second, Tom, went into engineering in the Midlands and the youngest, John, was sent to St. Catherine's College, Cambridge where he gained a B.A. degree and became a schoolmaster.

Unfortunately the farming at Ladbarrow came to an end when Tom died suddenly on his fifty-first birthday. His son, Robert, carried on for a year and then moved with his mother to a smaller farm at Taynton, near Burford.

Tom sometimes known as Reg

During the first quarter of the twentieth century while the farming affairs of Aldsworth had been going on with very little change, there were other members of the family who had become scattered. One of these was Tom, W.T.'s nephew, whose father had died of typhoid in 1905 when Tom was at school.

Tom (known as Reg by his mother till he left home) did not go in for farming, in fact very little is known of him as his marriage failed and he often lived alone, or abroad. Within a week of the outbreak of the Great War he was commissioned Second-Lieutenant in the Connought Rangers and served in France. In June of 1915 he transfered to the Royal Flying Corps and became a pilot. At the end of 1916 he resigned his commission, but from what cause is not known, but it could have been due to wounds.

Very little is known of him for the next twenty years although some of the time he was personal assistant to the Chief Engineer building railways and harbours in Persia. Then he served a two year contract on the same work in West Africa. He returned to England in the thirties and the depression. Then he lived on a boat on his own in the Thames Estuary doing hydrographic work and writing articles for magazines.

Tom Garne, 1915. (1890-1962.)

At the outbreak of the Second World War he was once more given a commission in the Connought Rangers as a Second-Lieutenant although nearly fifty years of age. He quickly became a captain in charge of transport at Aldershot at an officer training unit. In 1943 he transferred to the Royal Engineers as a captain.

After the war he returned to living alone on a boat in the Thames Estuary doing work as a hydrographer. When ill health finally forced him to live ashore, he rode large motor bikes, which he carried on doing until he was seventy. He died in 1962 aged 72.

Douglas

As we saw in the chapter on Burford Brewery when Arthur Garne died on Newmarket race-course his brother, Willie, took into partnership his cousin, Austen Hewer, so that Arthur's widow could be paid her half share.

Douglas was taken from school when he was nearly seventeen in the summer of 1905 and put to work in the brewery. He gradually learnt the practical side of brewing and although he was paid very little, after four years he assumed he was part of the firm. It came as somewhat of a shock therefore when his uncle told him there was no longer a job for him in the brewery as his cousin, Nelson, was going to give up his engineering training and come into the business.

So Arthur's widow, Melly, decided to rent a house in London so that her son, Douglas, could attend the "John Cass Institute" daily to study brewing chemistry and her two daughters could go to boarding school.

The plan, however, came to nothing when Douglas became very taken with the third daughter of the house in which they were staying in West Kensington. This was a boarding house run by a widow, who was a professional singer, with four daughters.

So Melly Garne took a house instead in Frenchay Road, Oxford with her two small girls. Douglas remained in London at the house of his fiancee until they were married in 1912 when he was twenty-three.

His first job was as underbrewer for Brandons of Putney and he and his wife, Mary Stringer, rented a house at East Sheen where their daughter, Myfanwy was born. In 1914 they moved to Abingdon where Douglas was underbrewer for Morlands. Here their son, Richard, was born while Douglas was doing war work for the ordnance factory at nearby Didcot. After the war they moved to Wateringbury in Kent to Leney's brewery. Leneys had been Shorthorn cattle breeders who sold

George Garne his stock bull, Grand Duke of Geneva 2nd, forty years earlier. The picture of this bull still hangs on the wall of Robert Handy's house at Hampen.

In 1923 Douglas was appointed head brewer for Thompson's of Walmer in East Kent where he remained till his sudden death from phlebitus in 1929, aged 41.

CHAPTER XII

The Second Half of the Twentieth Century

The gradual move away from farming as the main occupation of the family which had begun in the nineteenth century continued until there were no Garne farmers left in England.

This change was brought about by many different factors, better education, the desire for an easier life, better communications, smaller families, the upheaval brought about by the Second World War, the increased capital needed to start farming and the national change in the pattern of landlord and tenant making tenanted farms more difficult to find.

The end of Garne farming in England

The four main Garne farms at the outbreak of the Second World War were at Aldsworth, Taynton and Cam. To take Aldsworth first; decline here had been slow through the farming depression of the 20's and 30's. Will Garne would not change his system, methods or way of life. When war broke out in 1939, Will's only son, Billy, was twenty-four and should have been in a position to take over the farm and benefit from scarcity prices due to wartime conditions, but Billy was in the Wiltshire Yeomanry, so was immediately mobilised and posted to the middle-east with his horse, where he served throughout the war mostly with tanks.

Will could not face being told to plough grassland and concentrate on arable farming with mechanisation when his whole life had been breeding cattle and sheep. So in 1942 he gave up the tenancy of the Swyre Farm, which he had held for thiry years, and continued to farm very much as before with a large ageing workforce and very little mechanisation so that at the end of the war when he was sixty-five he was not in the prosperous position of most of his arable farming neighbours, many of whom were able to buy their farms from declining estates.

Gloucestershire - - - Cotswolds

BETWEEN CIRENCESTER AND BURFORD

"THE GREEN FARM"
ALDSWORTH

229 Acres

AUCTION — THURSDAY, 23rd MAY, 1968

Auctioneers:
Messrs. TAYLER & FLETCHER
The Square
STOW-ON-THE-WOLD, Glos.
(Tels. 383 & 384)

Solicitors:
Messrs. FRANCIS, WICKINS & HILL
The Square
STOW-ON-THE-WOLD, Glos.
(Tels. 621 & 332)

He had kept his Shorthorn herd with the oldest pedigree of any British herd and his Cotswold sheep flock, which for many years had been the only one in existence. The survival of this famous breed today can be entirely attributed to Will Garne's refusal to think of giving them up even though they were probably losing money. Their shepherd was still Jim Wilcox aged seventy-three at the end of the war. He had devoted his entire life to the flock and the interest of the Garne family as had his father before him. He is buried in an unmarked grave in Aldsworth churchyard having lived to be eighty-one.

Will Garne had been able to turn his skill as a judge of livestock, particularly cattle and sheep, to good account in the years before the war by becoming a partner in a business buying pedigee stock for export. This firm "British Livestock Exports" was able to restart directly after the war and take advantage of the demand for British stock.

In 1942 Will Garne bought an eighty acre, all grass farm at Meysey Hampton, a village eight miles from Aldsworth, from a Captain Dennis, where the tenant was Bertie Edmonds, a second cousin of Wills. The idea of this farm was for Will's son, Billy, to occupy the farmhouse when he returned from the war and married.

The farm was not an asset though which increased the farm income; this continued to decline so that in 1949 it was necessary to sell the Ablington Farm, a portion of the farm having been compulsorily purchased by the air ministry as a landing ground. The hundred odd acres, three cottages and farm buildings were sold at auction to a Mr. Jelf for £8,300 who resold it to Mr. S. J. Phillips who was tenant of Blackpitts Farm and many other local farms and who was buying farms wherever possible.

By this time four of Will and Frances's daughters had married, the eldest, Helen, to Newell A'Bear, a farmer in Berkshire, the next, Phyllis, to Robert Pike, also a Berkshire farmer. Pamela had married David Young, an agricultural engineer and Daphne, the youngest, to Peter West, a scientist. Barbara was unmarried as was the mainstay of the business, Sue, who still lived at home.

This slow decline at Aldsworth continued with very little change for another twenty years until Will's death in 1967 at the age of eighty-seven. When that happened Billy sold the farm, house and cottages and retired to Meysey Hampton having built a bungalow in the garden and orchard in the centre of the village of Aldsworth which had at one time

RELIC OF A GREAT PAST

THE Cotswolds have a larger recorded history than any other British breed of sheep. Leicester crosses on the ancient Cotswold fine middlewool type, made through last century, gave them such a new lease of life that, around 1858, they were one of the leading breeds in the showring. Now only one flock remains on the Cotswolds, in the possession of Mr. William Garne, aged 78, of Aldsworth, seen in the adjoining picture with his shepherd, Mr. John Bond (left). This Garne flock has a history of over 300 years, and rams from it are now being put on Half-Bred ewes with success.

been the rickyard of the Green Farm. This bungalow, occupied by Will's widow, Frances, and her single daughter, Sue, maintained the Garne presence in Aldsworth. Although in fact it was the end of an era of Garne farming in Aldsworth which had lasted for one hundred and sixty-seven years.

Barbara, Will's forth daughter, had married her cousin, Richard Garne of the Burford Branch, who became manager of a large farm at Winson, for Colonel Robert Henriques, seven miles from Aldsworth; thus reuniting two branches of the Garne family after one hundred and fifty years. Richard had been brought up in Kent and had only briefly met his distant cousins at Aldsworth before joining the army at the beginning of the war. This he spent mostly in Burma and was demobilised with the rank of Major. Two children were born to this union, Susan and Timothy.

Cocklebarrow the other Garne farm in Aldsworth had been given up by Arthur Garne in 1947 although he and his wife, Nelsie, remained in the farmhouse for a few more years farming fifty acres with pigs and poultry before moving to a house in the village. Their only child, Joan, married Oscar Colburn, a farmer from neighbouring Crickleybarrow, in 1950. He later became nationally famous as a breeder of sheep and cattle and also became a Queen's Commissioner.

At *Taynton* eight miles away, Robert had married Dorothy Whitford. They had two children, George and Vivian. When Robert retired, the tenancy of the farm was given up, George having followed different occupations. Few landlords would allow farmer's sons to carry on a tenancy, it was also becoming more difficult for young men with modest capital to start farming on their own account.

Robert's brother, Tom, had become an engineer in the Midlands and married Dorothy Jones. They had no children of their own but adopted a boy, Jeremy.

Robert's youngest brother, John, had enlisted in the Royal Horse Guards on the outbreak of war, was commissioned in the Rifle Brigade, awarded the M.C. in France and demobilised as a Major. He married Betti Maynard and they had two children, Adrian and Brigid. John was appointed Director of Education for Oxfordshire and when he retired a street in Oxford was named after him, John Garne Way.

Cam

The pattern of movement away from farming was the same at

Church Farm, Cam. Ben ran the farm in partnership with his father, Charles, who lived to be eighty-six. Ben and Joyce had no sons, so soon after Charles's death the farm was given up.

Conclusion

So today (1984) the young men who have inherited the good name of Garne and the qualities of their yeoman ancestors, however much diluted, are few in number and scattered a long way from their origins in Gloucestershire. In my view if people are to take responsibility for the future it is of great value to know the past history of one's family and where one's roots go back to.

All those in this generation have an entirely different background to those of previous generations. They were born into an entirely different world and also away from the background of farming, which had been the whole life of countless generations of Garnes back to the middle ages. This is with the sole exception of the Garn branch in Western Australia: although two of the young generation of English Garnes were born on farms they followed different occupations later. The enormous changes which had slowly taken place in British farming over the previous fifty years were over before the present generation were born.

Index

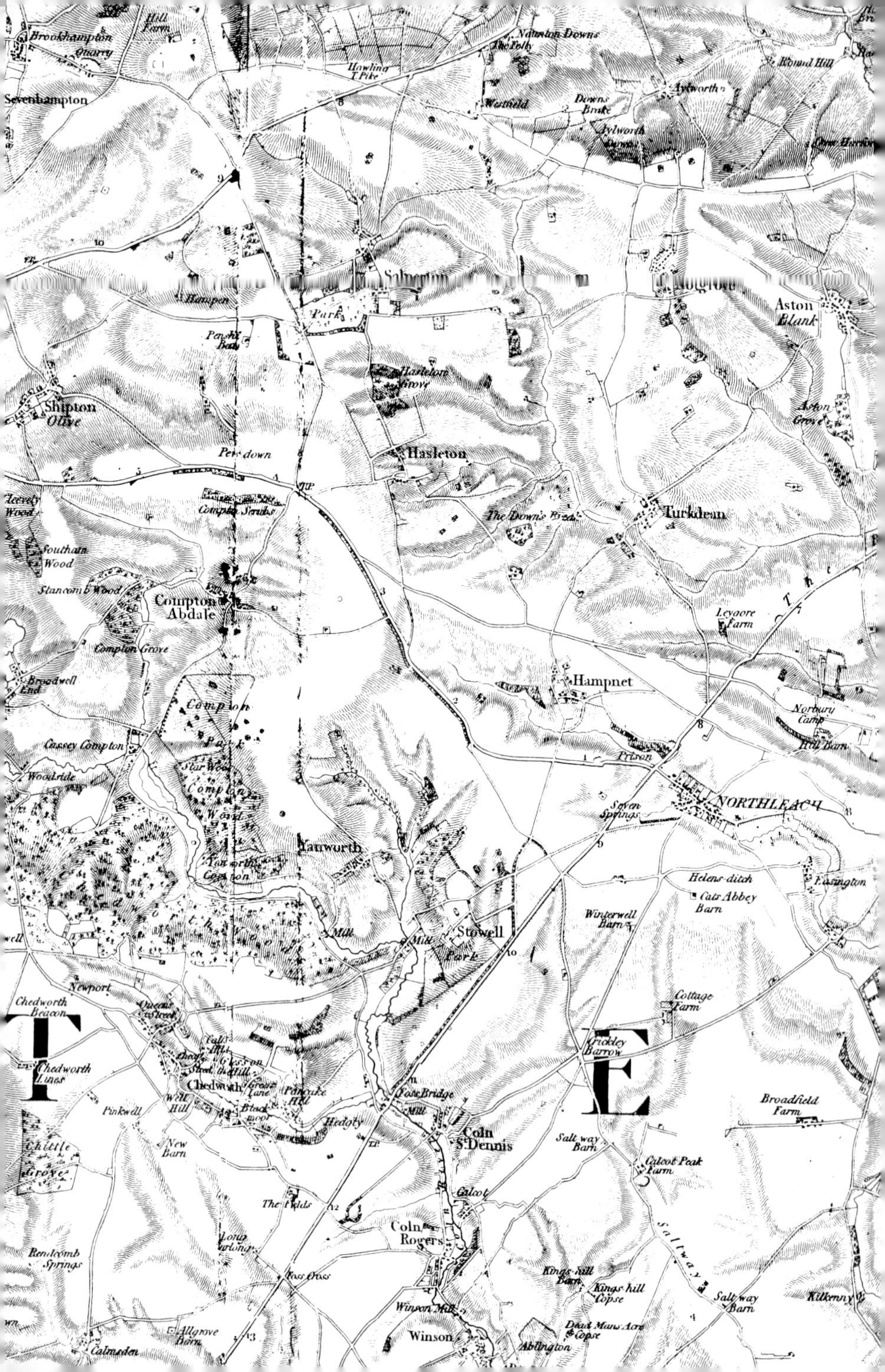
Brookhampton
Quarry
Hill Farm
Sevenhampton
Naunton Downs
The Folly
Hawling T.Pike
Round Hill
Aylworth
Downs
Aylworth
Hampen
Park
Aston Blank
Shipton Olive
Haslet on Grove
Hasleton
Aston Grove
Pew down
Compton Scrubs
The Downs
Turkdean
Southam Wood
Stancomb Wood
Compton Abdale
Leygore Farm
Compton Grove
Broadwell End
Hampnet
Compton Park
Norbury Camp
Cassey Compton
Hill Barn
Woodride
Star Wood
Compton Wood
Prison
Seven Springs
NORTHLEACH
Yanworth
Yanworth Common
Helens ditch
Eastington
Cats Abbey Barn
Winterwell Barn
Mill
Stowell
Park
Newport
Chedworth Beacon
Cottage Farm
T
Chedworth Lines
Chedworth
Pancake Hill
Crickley Barrow
E
Foss Bridge
Pinkwell
Hedgty
Broadfield Farm
Chittle Grove
New Barn
Coln St. Dennis
Saltway Barn
Calcot Peak Farm
The Fields
Calcot
Coln Rogers
Rendcomb Springs
Saltway
Foss Cross
Kings hill Barn
Kings hill Copse
Salt way Barn
Kilkenny
Winson Mill
Allgrove Barn
Dead Mans Acre Copse
Winson
Calmsden
Ablington